WORKS IN PROGRESS

A COLLECTION OF WORK CREATED BY
THE TALENT OF THE FUTURE

CONTRIBUTIONS

Thank you to all our wonderful contributors, without whom this project would not have been possible!

Jackie McPhereson

Abby Grewal

John & Schmuncle

Lisbeth Gullaksen Lunde

Phil & Lynn Reed

Arman Sadeghpour

Angelo Chioda

Dorian & Micaela Benntt

Anna Pirovano

Michael Valentino

Pam Cavin & Michael Thompson

Tom Reagan

Lorenzo Pirola

Depop Ltd.

Tina Freeman

Jay & Miggy Monroe

Lambert & Bond

Alexa Georges

Ducky Nguyen

Craig McDonald

Eduardo Morales

Gordon Jackson

Runar Reistrup

Maria Raga

Mercedes Fast

Raisa Luck

Kai-Eivind Marthinussen

James Comyn

Costanza Beltrami

Derek Neiberger

Tainá Vilela

Joan Costello

Margo DuBos

Anna Ku

Nikki Padilla

Donna Sutton

Paul & Sarah Harris

Patricia Bernstein

Maricarmen Christensen

Simonne Mcivor

Cody Pumper

Amit Chuahan

John R Mangiardi

Audrey Muir

Louise Locock

Jan Inge Meling

Jamie Ortega

Yutetsu Ametani

Marguerite Lewis

Lea Beglerovic

Stephanie Leone

Arnaud Tanguy

Nicolae Namolovan

Bruyle

Giorgia Negroni

Ed Tribe

Nicola Keys

Linda Green

Victoria Trelinksa

Elle Hobkirk

Scott Gargan

Grace Wagner

Christian Ashton

Veronica Comin

Domenico D'Ercole

Kamilla Lucarelli

Henry St. Leger Davey

Bea Svistunenko

Guy Clark

Karianne Gullaksen Lunde

James Hansen

Isolde Penwarden

Zoe Sharples

Atri Banerjee

Tommaso Genovesi

© TIZIANA PESENTI

ABOUT THE PROJECT

WORKS IN PROGRESS is an innovative multimedia project made up of a collection of short stories and poems written by graduates of prestigious New York Creative Writing courses. Each piece is accompanied by illustrations and music from an international collective of young and talented artists. QR codes have been integrated throughout the book, which will link readers to a webpage created for the project, resulting in a unique reading experience that combines the joys of print and digital storytelling.

The collection was curated and published by a group of aspiring publishers on University College London's MA in Publishing course. They have worked tirelessly to create a collection that they hope shines a light on aspiring new talent.

ABOUT THE PUBLISHERS

The WORKS IN PROGRESS team are all
currently working towards achieving Masters in
Publishing at University College London.

DELIA CAROLINE BENNETT

An American living in London, Delia is a graduate of
The New School in New York and is currently on the MA
Publishing course hoping to turn her passion for tech and
books into a thriving career in publishing. Her literary interests
lay in digital innovations in publishing, YA Fiction, cookery
books, and Edward Snowden's Twitter feed.

SYDNEY BUTLER

Sydney is originally from Gorham, Maine. She completed
her undergraduate at Wellesley College, earning degrees in
both English and psychology. She is interested in examining
how data and new technologies can be leveraged to make
information accessible to more diverse audiences. Her
favorite authors include Charlotte Brontë, Margaret Atwood,
and Kazuo Ishiguro.

ALEX HARRISON

Alex is an aspiring editor with a particular interest in the
science fiction and fantasy market. He divides his time between
reading, writing, food, and playing real-life quidditch.

Nisha Emich

Born in Vienna to Dutch and Malaysian parents and growing up in the Czech Republic, Nisha loves to travel and meet new people. She graduated from Cambridge University with a degree in English Literature, and has interned at Simon & Schuster, Bloomsbury, and Hachette. Her favourite things to read include cookbooks and feminist tirades.

Camilla Lunde

Camilla is an aspiring editor and future publisher. She has a MA with Honours in English Literature and History from the University of Edinburgh. Camilla has experience as a freelance editor and has interned with Octopus Books as an editorial assistant. In the future, she hopes to work for a non-fiction trade publisher specialising in sports and popular culture.

Silvia Pirola

After graduating in Humanities at Università degli Studi di Milano, Silvia moved to London. In her research, she is focusing on learning environments and the effects of new devices on reading habits. She is combining her research interests with her curiosity for new technologies and her work as an intern at HarperCollins in the Rights Department.

Hannah Reed

Hannah received a 2:1 BA in graphic arts majoring in illustration at Winchester School of Art, University of Southampton. She also has commissioned and published by the Conde Nast Traveller, and has work experience with Ella & Otto and National Portrait Gallery Publishing. She is heavily interested in illustration and design and hopes to move into the design field of publishing.

TABLE OF CONTENTS

A NOTE ABOUT QR CODES

At the start of every story there is a title page featuring an illustration, and a page with a QR code generated specifically for the work. By scanning the QR code with a smartphone or tablet, readers will be taken to a personalized page on the WORKS IN PROJECT website where they can see the full illustration in colour, and learn more about the artist who created it. There are a number of free QR scanner apps available for download online.

The website will contain further details about the author of each story as well. Finally, the publishers have curated a song to accompany each individual story, which readers can listen to online. Information about the musicians featured for the project will also be listed on the website. The QR code on the following page will bring readers directly to the homepage of the WORKS IN PROGRESS website.

SELECTED POETRY

KATHERINE DELUCA

CORONA; QUEENS

He's afraid of the way the glass blows,
the way houses are layered here
like locker-rooms. It would've been okay
if I'd just said goodbye,
but we're all a little fractured.

Patching up

stairwells and watering holes,
layered houses—hot sauce
in the steam pot. This sofa was alive
that day. Breathing and balding,
bathed in indigo

conscious of its short legs, short-lived
symphonies. He read my mind once.
Unopened buttons, layered houses.
There was nothing not to like
about that morning.

ALONE IN MY BUNGALOW

Alone in my bungalow.
Embers spill from a citrus-scented candle
by the window next to the bed.
Its orange flesh melts quicker and quicker
back into itself, and I am reminded
of what it's like to get stuck on a thought

like the one where you and I stare hopelessly into each other
at that brick-walled coffee shop in Cobble Hill.
You smell like flower and curated memories,
marble eyes tinged with needlepoint darkness.
You tell me if I don't like
the way an orchid wilts,
don't look at it.

A cat rustles beneath the bed—I am back in my bungalow,
hands numbed from early March winds
that leak through the window pane.
And as my back presses against thin, lacerated pillows,
I think only of dry lips that sip cigarettes,
and how damn good you look when it snows.

THE PHOTOGRAPH

I thought of the time I found the photograph of you
and her, lying across your sheets that I'd washed
in the laundromat on Bedford Ave days before.
How enticed you were with her exotic style—
six inch heels, a skirt taut across her thighs
like fish skin, braless.

What's worse than the still night,
and her black body draped over your bedspread,
while I drive home to half-stained coffee mugs
and a carton of Reds that are never enough
to burn, the way she did then,
carving shapes between your legs.

Her prison eyes possessed you
more than our velveteen sheets and
crisp pillow cases, more than my
fingertips buried beneath the loose
skin on your shoulders.

As I lifted the photograph from the sheets,
I grew numb. And still, wished it were me
in that picture, staring at the untrimmed hairs
that curl above your lips. Just to be there—
running my fingers through your
thin, disheveled hair.

To The Pigeon Man at Washington Square Park

A red-tailed hawk, perched above the Kimmel
building of NYU, eyes its prey, ignoring
the ruckus of yellow cabs and raggedy men
rummaging through stale garbage pails.

A man stands in front of the arch.
He has hair like shoe strings, a missing tooth.
The pigeons walk lightly and nibble along
the dusty sleeves of his burlap coat.

He holds them close to his face, stroking
their feathers against his rough cheeks:
a lion kissing his lioness in a hollow cave.
Any act of affection, something to show

how he traded seersucker suits, ties,
a wedding ring, and coffee mugs

for time with the pigeons in early spring,
when icicles melt from the arch,
and musicians unbuckle cases
that hold their flutes and trombones.

FLUSHING AVENUE IN SPRING

When daylight shrinks, it forgets how it used
to warm bare-backs and give orchids their color.

Now, it's March in the city, and I've been
waiting too long to unbutton my coat.

It's still gray and naked when I walk
past leafless shrubs down the street to work.
The tree branches, so long and barren—
like praying hands in an empty church.

But there you are, in a green sweatshirt smoking
a cigarette, holding the door open for me as I step
inside Jimmy's Deli on the corner of Flushing

and Dekalb. It's then that I see the daffodils
in planters on the sides of the road, giving
a little color to the littered streets.

For the Man Playing the Trumpet on the G-Train Platform

The gypsy holds her cloth sack with panic.
The children seem more rowdy this year.
Broken bottles and diseased kisses and no one
wants to take care of them. Daydreamers
take note of this year's flower, the fainted orchid.
It's good to know children have a home in Brooklyn.

The dead grass is more shapely there,
and fathers and whores merge in the stale
ends of the park, where dust covers layers
of the clean night. At dusk the handprints
return, but no one notices them. Oblivion
walks beneath the trees where squirrels curl
under for winter. I see a rat's head poking out
from the smashed pumpkin on the train tracks.

His face reminds me of someone I knew
when I was sixteen and had a home, a fire-place
filled colonial that stood overlooking a golf course.
Now, I rinse memories away with each new raindrop
that comes in from the west. The trumpet starts up
and my feet fail to match its beat. The mind is

beautiful, isn't it? How it hits and chases
itself, how it burns and flails.

Walking Across The Williamsburg Bridge

The rods holding the bridge were
rusted and coated in dust,
like the extra forks and knives you
keep hidden in your apartment
under the sink that leaks
every time you turn the right knob.

We were pedestrians in the bicycle lane,
causing loud shouts and ringing bells.
It wasn't fair they had the better view of Manhattan,
gray silhouettes of skyscrapers against a setting sun,
while the people on foot had to stare at New Jersey,
its run-down buildings and yellow musk.

I suggested we walk where all the other walkers did,
but you complained about all the trash, each piece
of litter – a two-hundred dollar fine. And besides,
you'd seen all the graffiti on that side already.

You'd rather gamble, "Who are they to tell us
where we're allowed to walk?"
I watched your hair flap when the J train
passed us on the tracks to our left.

By the time we reached the bridge's ending slope
we'd walked a mile and a half in dim light.
I took off my jacket, the one I stole from my mom
before I left for college in September,

and we continued walking hand-in-hand until
we reached a bar on 13th, where we drank
three Bourbons each, the liquor hot
and burning in our mouths.

NOT CLINT EASTWOOD

WHITMAN BEDWELL

Not Clint Eastwood

In the week after I graduated from San Bernardino High School, two things happened, which no one saw coming, but that were very important to my brother and I. First, my mother died from a cancer no one knew she had. Stomach cancer is hard to see. Second, we got a life insurance check in the mail for fifty thousand dollars. Nobody knew she had that either.

After the funeral that we told nobody about, and where I had to pull my brother away from the grave, we spent a thousand dollars on a beat up 1991 Oldsmobile Cutlass. My brother and I packed everything we needed from the apartment into it. We stopped at the Shell Station off of Highway 210 where my brother worked. He told his boss to go fuck himself, that he was rich now, and then we left town.

For the next year or so we did nothing but move. We moved from small town to small town, all over the country, looking to see places we never thought we'd get to see. Hell, anywhere out of Berdoo was a surprise. But we wasted it. We wasted the sights and the places, and did the same damn things we'd always done. We wasted the money, pretty much all of it, on cheap motels and cheap bars and cheap women. We loved it, and our love of all that sameness bordered on fanaticism. That life, in the dirt and in the dirty, was us. For a whole year we were as happy as a preacher on Sunday, living a life of waste and making ourselves superstars of the seediest congregation.

There were a lot of things that happened, but none of them were of substance. Not until I woke up one morning in a town in West Texas, a couple hours outside of El Paso, stepped outside of the motel room to have a cigarette, and realized I hated myself.

All I had were matches, and half the pack ended up burnt out and on the ground before I could light my cigarette. I sat on the curb in front of the motel room and watched the cars inch down the highway. There were thousands of people spending their mornings going almost nowhere just to get somewhere, and, for the first time in a long time, I wished I had somewhere I had to be.

The door opened behind me, and I turned and saw my brother walking over in his underwear. He was pale, and his body thin like a young girl's. But his eyes were sharp and mean and couldn't hide his hardness. He sat down on the curb next to me and took one of my cigarettes, lighting it with one match on the first try.

"I don't know how you're awake," he said. "How long were you up last night?"

"I'm still up," I said.

He gave me an angry look, and moved his eyes everywhere but into my own. He took a long drag of his cigarette and held down the smoke, letting it swell up in his chest. Then he let it go, and in the same breath started talking, unfortunately, about my drug habit.

"You need to lay off that shit," he said, and tapped his nose with his index finger.

"Don't worry about me," I answered. "I'll get it under control. You did, and I've got more will than you."

I wanted to make him mad, maybe even mad enough to take a swing at me. But he smiled and grabbed me by the back of the neck.

14

"All right," he said. "I'll lay off you about it, just try to lay off it a little more, all right?" He laughed and stood up in front of me. "I don't want to get stuck in some town like this while you put that shit up your nose every night. One day your mind will fall right out of your ass, and then what the hell am I going to do?"

I knew he was joking, but I didn't think he was funny. When he put it that way, it made me feel like an addict and it made me upset. But I didn't show him that. That was weakness, so instead I grinned and gave him the finger. I wasn't going to apologize and I was too tired to argue and have him treat me as if I was his kid, not his kid brother. He shadow boxed me with his cigarette in his hand and let the burning end of it come closer and closer to my face until I pulled away from him.

"How much did we spend on the room?" I asked.

"Don't worry about it," he said. "I took care of it. That creep at the front desk gave us a real good deal thanks to you and your little problem. I gave him two grams and he took care of it for us. He's a real creep, though. Did I tell you what he asked me last night? He asked me about 'the boy' I checked in with. I think he wants to fuck you." He grinned, and I didn't feel as bad or as upset as I did before. My brother could be funny like that, could change the air and the energy of a place or a person in a second.

"Shut up," I said. I tried to hold in a laugh, but I couldn't. My brother tossed his cigarette at my feet and I stepped on it and then put out what was left of mine.

We went back into the room. I laid down on the cheap bed and wondered what types of people had laid down on it before, leaving behind something foul that I couldn't see but was still rolling around in. My brother took off his underwear at the door and walked passed me, naked, into the bathroom.

"Seriously, let's get out of here before that guy or some

weirdo does something to us," he said. "I don't want to be the inspiration for one of those shitty crime shows. And I can't take another day of no air conditioning. What the fuck kind of motel has no air conditioning?"

"The kind where you can trade coke for a room to the front desk freak who wants to fuck your brother."

He shut the bathroom door and turned on the sink and the shower, but I could hear him throwing up anyway.

***

We left the motel right at noon and stopped at the diner on the next corner. It was small; there was one row of booths, a counter that ran down the whole length of the building, and a kitchen in the back. There were dozens of pictures hung up on the walls, and each one was a picture of Clint Eastwood. No one else, just him, and he stared down at me from so many different angles. Clint Eastwood surrounded me. He was a cop in some pictures and a gun fighter in others, but he was tough in all of them.

I could've spent all day staring at those photos of Clint Eastwood, but the smell of food hit me and it hit me hard. I knew the food was good because I could see how greasy it was in the pictures on the menu, and diner food was the best when it was soaked in grease. It reminded me of home and my dead mother, when all we had was her knowing how to make real good food with almost nothing to make it from.

We waited too long for the waitress to take our order, and it made my brother mad. He tapped his spoon on the countertop and clenched his jaw. The longer we waited the faster he tapped, the harder he clenched. When the waitress came up to us, I saw that she was young and pretty. Her face was round and she had curves. I smiled at her, but she didn't smile back. She watched my brother tap his spoon for a moment and asked us what we were having. I knew she thought we were nothing and that she would forget us as soon as we left.

It was noon and my brother ordered a beer. I looked at him the way he looked at me on the curb earlier, and he shrugged. He had no control over it. The waitress brought the beer and a glass of water for me. My brother drank the beer quickly, without enjoyment.

"You see her slam our drinks down on the table?" he asked. "She just slammed them down with her chubby fingers. She has little sausage fingers."

"Leave her alone," I said.

"No. She can't be rude to us just because she's fat and has sausage fingers. You can always tell who the fat ones are. They can hide it by wearing black and wearing loose clothes. But they can't hide their round faces and their chubby, sausage fingers."

The waitress walked by again and he grabbed her arm and handed her the empty bottle.

"I'd like another one, sweetheart." She frowned at him and took the bottle away.

"Sausage Fingers doesn't like me too much. What a fat little cunt."

"She's not fat," I said. "She's just not skinny."

"Well, look at you being nice. What a charmer! You should go talk to her."

"For what?" The beer was taking over his eyes, and I knew that he was about to get real mean.

"Go talk to Sausage Fingers," he said, loudly, his grin as big as it ever got. "See when Sausage Fingers gets off, and maybe we can wait around. Maybe she'll let you fuck her in her car or something. And then maybe you won't be so god-damn wound up all the time."

"I don't want to wait around. Not around here. Not with you acting like this." I wished he would stop, but his eyes told

17

me he wouldn't.

"You need a girl, I'm telling you. You haven't been with one since we left home. What was that little whore's name? Was it Erica?"

He kept going on about it, but I stopped listening. I looked up at Clint Eastwood, all of him. I wished I could be him. Girls loved Clint Eastwood. They loved him fully and completely, as if he was the most important and impressive person they could ever have. Clint Eastwood drank, but only when he needed too. He always won. He was confident. He knew where he was going, what he had to do, and he got there and he did it. Even when he wasn't going anywhere in particular, wherever he ended up was where the action was. And he was always on the right side of that action. He was everything that I wasn't. I could feel all of those Clint Eastwoods staring at me and judging me. I was no Clint Eastwood.

The waitress brought another beer, and my brother said, "Thanks, beautiful. You're a doll. Not a nice one, but still a doll." She avoided his gaze and then walked away uneasily.

"You going to try and fuck her or not?" he asked.

"You should fuck her," I said. "And if you can't get it up, maybe you should fuck yourself."

"Oh, don't be so sore. We're just having a little fun, that's all. Even Sausage Fingers is having fun."

I said nothing else. I knew the food would be coming out soon, but I wasn't hungry anymore. I pulled a twenty from my pocket, placed it on the table, and walked outside to smoke and get away from the great Clint Eastwood, Sausage Fingers, and my drunk brother. I finished my cigarette and walked to the car to wait for him to finish as many beers as they'd serve him. When he came back to the car, he was drunk, said something about, "A bunch of motherfuckers," and turned the radio on.

We decided to leave town and were almost to the highway

18

when we stopped at a red light in a bad part of town. A bum stood at the intersection, holding up a sign that said something about him being down on his luck and willing to do anything for food.

My brother rolled down the window.

"You want some money?" he said.

"I'll take anything," said the bum. "I'll do anything."

"Then let me spit on you," my brother said.

"What?"

"You heard me. Let me spit on you. I'm feeling a little sick. Let me hock one back, and let me spit it right in your face. I'll give you a ten dollar bill."

The bum's worn face looked hateful. "Fuck you," he said, his voice dead flat.

My brother opened the door and got out of the car. I called after him and told him to stop and get back in but he was drunk and uncaring.

"Excuse me," my brother said. "I know you didn't just say what I think you just said." The bum leaned away from the traffic pole. He was old and broken. He wore a parka over a sweatshirt even though it was very hot, and his face was weathered and burned by a long time spent in the sun. That face twisted in confusion as my brother came toward him. He walked away slowly, with a limp, and my brother followed him.

I watched them from the rear-view mirror. They seemed to be playing a game, yelling at one another, but never gaining or losing any ground on the other. My brother followed the bum around a corner, and I knew the only thing I could do was sit in the car and wait. A few minutes went by and I began to worry. I changed the radio station but found nothing I felt like listening to. I wished I had a bump then. I wanted to drive around the block and find a liquor store or a bar, and just run in real quick and have one drink, but I was afraid my brother would be back before I was and he'd be mad and I'd have to fight him or listen to him bitch.

I was still thinking about how nice a bump or even a drink would be when I heard a noise outside the car. I saw the old bum pass by the window, fast on the move despite his limp. He moved forward but kept his eyes on whatever was behind him.

My brother yelled from behind the car. "Get him." I glanced in the mirror again and saw him running toward the car with his hand over his face. His hand and white shirt were covered in blood. "Hurry up and get that son of a bitch."

I got out without thinking, moving on instinct, and chased the man. It wasn't much of a chase with his gimpy leg, and even though he had a head start I caught him by the end of the next block. I came up behind him and kicked one of his feet. His legs tangled together and he fell, hard. His head thumped against the ground like a ball bouncing off a wall. He sprawled out, face down on the concrete, and I saw that his clothes were dusty and worn through with holes, and I was glad I didn't have to really touch him.

He started to crawl. I didn't know what to do, so I walked along side of him. He cursed me, called me a motherfucker. My brother found his way to us not long after. He was very drunk and very angry.

My brother was out of breath but he was grinning. His teeth were red from all the blood that had fallen across his face. His shirt was off and he held it up against his eye.

"This fucker had a lead pipe under his jacket. He hit me with it. Fiend faggot. No respect for anybody."

He kicked the bum in his side, and a small moan came from the ground. My brother kicked him again, harder this time. A sharp gasp for air replaced the moan.

"Sure, I can't believe he didn't respect you," I said. "With you wanting to spit on him and all."

My brother's eyes lit up with rage. I felt sorry for the man and sorry for my brother. His head was still bleeding, and when the shirt slipped down a little bit as he kicked the bum, I saw a long deep gash across his left eyebrow.

"Let's go," I said. "Let's go before you do something stupid and before it's too late to keep going and get out of here."

My brother didn't hear me, because he didn't want to listen. He paced around the bum.

"You need to get that cut cleaned up." I said. "You started the whole damn thing."

He heard me then and looked into my eyes, and I saw his hatred lessen. He reached into the man's pockets. He found a little bit of money and counted it up where I could see. It was twelve dollars. He put it in his back pocket and walked backed toward the car.

"Don't take that," I said. "Leave him his twelve dollars."

"He's got to pay. He split my face open, and I'm not going to beat him to death, so he's got to pay somehow. Everybody's got to pay for something."

"It looks like you were the one who paid for being such a goddamned asshole. And, you beat him pretty bad."

"No," he said. "*We* beat him pretty bad. You caught him and you made him hit his head. You're as guilty as I am."

He was right. I wished I'd never listened to him and gotten out of the car.

He turned to the bum lying in the street. "You're lucky I don't kill you. I should, and you'd deserve it. I could do it, right here in the middle of the street in broad daylight, and I'd get away with it, too. I'd never even think about you again. Nobody would."

He was right about everything he'd said. I felt a guilty pride and power puff up in my throat. Then it went away, real quick.

We left the town and hit the highway, headed south toward the border. It was getting dark, and the sky turned from blue to

21

yellow and then to purple. I didn't like when the sky did that. It made the changing of days so obvious and so many of them made me feel as if I was wasting away, drunk and unable to feel for anyone or anything. My whole body was numb. I was driving too fast, but I couldn't take my foot off the gas pedal. I pressed down and felt nothing, so I pressed harder, hoping that feeling would come back, that I would find an edge I cared to not cross. It was there, somewhere, and the only way I could find it was to go faster and farther. I had to push. I sank all I had into the road and hoped that feeling would come before I crossed over a line from which I wouldn't be able to return.

My brother wasn't afraid. He was as drunk and as numb as I was but he could care less about finding a feeling. He laughed as I sped up into the darkness of the empty highway. I didn't dare look at him. His eyes were still red and angry. He wanted to be numb and be forever this drunk and fucked up and too dumb to fear and sense. We sat in that car, going over a hundred, and I prayed that no matter how close we came to going over the edge, something would save us and slow us down and remind us it was okay to want to slow ourselves.

I started to feel it when the tires wobbled from the speed, but it wasn't all the way there yet. I needed to go faster. I heard us moving. The car rang in my ears, and it burned. The burning filled my whole head and got hotter and hotter, but I refused to stop the car or ease up on the pedal. I went faster, and the burning in my head began to flow through my entire body, and I shook as I drove. I wanted to stop, but it was out of my control. I was so close to feeling again, but close wasn't good enough.

The headlights hardly kept up with the spinning tires. They pushed along the beaten down highway, like lightning flashing and burning out before I could fully see it. The engine roared and yelled at us to see it and to hear its power. It dared me to keep going, and told me it wouldn't quit until I did. I

22

wasn't going to quit. I was determined to feel again. Then we were parked somewhere far out in the desert, away from everyone and everything except for the darkness and each other, and I fell asleep.

When I woke, the desert sprawled out in front of me in every direction. There was only the blackness of the night and the hardness of the desert floor. I felt sober and all right. Out there, in the black desert night, I was on a different planet. There was no cheap motel to check into, no bars, and none of the pretty ladies of the night. That night the desert was my home, and as I stared up into the sky, stars filled my sober head, millions and millions of them. They shined so bright against the blackness of space, like the most beautiful neon sign I'd ever seen. I realized I could feel again. I felt so damn alone, and then I felt that the loneliness right there in that spot was the most wonderful feeling I'd ever had.

I looked over at my brother. He was drunk and passed out next to the car. The drive had torn out of him all he'd had, and still he couldn't feel. I understood that we were separated forever then and there, like two different species that were unable to mate. I breathed in an air that he did not.

I loved him anyway. I loved that no matter how fucked up he got or what dumb thing he did, he always made sure we were together. But he was different, and he was getting worse. Our mother's death and a year of living like heathens took all of his beauty away. He wasn't my brother anymore. He was empty, and it made me sick. He wasn't ever going to not be a heathen.

"You have to run," I said to myself. I looked to see if my brother stirred when I broke the silence of the black desert, but he did not. "You have to run," I said again, and thinking about running made me smile. "You have to run!" I yelled it, and I laughed for a long time. I didn't know where I was going to go, or how I would get there, but I didn't care.

I stood up against that hard desert floor and looked up at the black horizon. I closed my eyes and spun around and around, like a little kid on a make believe carousel. When I opened my eyes, I couldn't tell which direction I was facing, but I decided that was the direction I would go.

I went back to the car and took half the money and my coat. I walked around to the side where my brother slept, and stood over him for what felt like a long time. I was found and he was lost, and I knew that he would never find himself. He was worse than the bum we beat in the alley. He was worse than the waitress that took us for dirt. He was worse than the pervert who worked at the motel.

I didn't know if I should say goodbye, and for a second I thought it would be best to kill him to spare the world the trouble, and spare him the trouble of the world. I picked up a rock and held it over him. I dropped it.

"Fuck you," I said. "Maybe you'll get it and then I'll see you again." It was the blackest time of the night, but I could feel that the sun would rise up soon. I turned in the direction I had decided upon and began to run. Slowly, I ran, and it was cold at first, but I sped up and I laughed and I felt warmth. I was afraid of moving through that darkness, but at least I was going somewhere, even if it was to nowhere in particular.

TIGHT

MEG ROWLAND

TIGHT

"Nineteen," I answered.

"Isn't that a little old?" she asked. I was talking to an older woman, a professor. "I mean, don't people in your generation lose their virginity younger than that?" She was right, and I was embarrassed. Not because I was nineteen when I lost my virginity, but because I lied: I had actually been twenty-one.

I hadn't waited to lose my virginity for any romantic or meaningful reasons. I didn't believe in saving yourself for marriage, I wasn't waiting to find someone deserving of my special flower, and I didn't have an Internet boyfriend somewhere I was saving babysitting money to go lose it to. I waited until I was twenty-one to have sex for the same reason I waited until the power was turned off to pay my ConEd bill—procrastination. When my friends started losing their virginities in high school, I was perfectly content with turning my schoolwork in on time, staying on top of the college hunt, and not having a burning UTI every weekend.

Eventually I lost my virginity about a month before my twenty-second birthday, to an old friend from high school, Dan. I hung out in two social circles in high school: a group of pretty, manicured housewives-in-training who called themselves The Poodles, and The Stoners. Dan was a Stoner. I never felt fully comfortable in either circle. I was too stoned and sardonic for The Poodles; too genuinely interested in how my eye makeup looked for The Stoners. But I clicked with Dan.

Over years of friendship, we'd occasionally get together and make out, but nothing really progressed past that, which I was fine with—it was weird to think about sleeping with someone I'd known since seventh grade. That is until one night during our senior year of college when Dan came to visit—and came prepared.

"What is this?" I asked as he slid over some kind of chart to me; it looked like a diagram explaining the governmental separation of powers. We were squished next to each other at a crowded bar.

"This," he said, "is a chart I found online that explains the Harry Met Sally Principle: it is virtually impossible for a man and a woman to be platonic friends. They *need* to have sex at some point."

"You brought a flow chart to a bar?"

"Fuck the flow chart, are you listening to me? I'm saying I think we should have sex tonight."

Dan reached down and put his hand on my thigh, which I slapped away so I could properly study his research. The chart was bullshit in the manner of most online theories, but my hymen had been burning a hole in my pocket for a while and nobody had ever tried to seduce me with an infographic, so I shrugged, figuring tonight might as well be The Night.

I didn't remember a lot about losing my virginity to Dan. I wasn't sure if that's because I was that drunk or that nervous...probably a combination of both. But I remember it hurting. More than I had been taught to expect. When Dan entered me on my little twin bed, I saw stars. Not because I was drowning in a sea of ecstasy, but because it felt as if my vagina was being cleaved in half. Pain seared through my pelvis, my eyes began to water, and I gasped for air. Unaware that I was a virgin and misinterpreting my pain for pleasure, Dan pushed back my legs until my knees were next to my ears, grabbed the headboard with both hands and began to fuck me hard. I was in so much pain I wanted to throw up. Right before I thought I would pass out before I could tell him to stop, he pulled out.

"You're too tight," he said, slightly annoyed. "But I'm close. Can I jerk off on your tits?" It wasn't poetic, but I was grateful he was out of me and even more grateful it was almost over. "Help yourself," I said, laying out the metaphorical welcome mat.

When I woke up the next morning, Dan was gone and I felt as if a thousand tiny Hindenburgs had attacked my crotch. Waves of sharp pain radiated from my vagina, and when I went to pee, nothing came out. I closed my eyes, tried to relax my PC muscles, and finally produced a small stream of urine that felt as if I was pissing cocktail swords. I remembered what Dan had said the night before. *You're too tight.* I sat there on the toilet for a while, defeated. I was wondering how mad my roommate would be if I spent the rest of the day with one of her bags of frozen turkey meatballs shoved down my pants when it dawned on me what I had to do: I had to have sex with everybody. I remembered when my friends lost their virginities nearly half a decade earlier. They'd said that sex hurt less the more they did it. So, with an uncharacteristic amount of motivation, I set out to do it. And I did it. A lot. Over the next month I had sex with old flings, I had sex with friends, I had sex with Dan again, I had sex with Dan's roommate—also, confusingly, named Dan. I had sex with a stranger on Friday night, sex with an old crush on Saturday. At the end of my month of erotic liberation, I reached an unexpected and unalterable outcome: sex was unbearably painful and it wasn't going to get better.

Around the same time, I happened to have an appointment with my gynecologist for my yearly exam and figured I would take that opportunity to ask her why sex was so painful for me. I waited for over an hour to see my doctor, and at the end

31

of the exam, she hurriedly snapped off her latex gloves and asked, "So do you have any questions or anything?" one foot literally out the door.

"Actually, yes," I said. "Um, I don't really know how to say this, but sex, like, *hurts*. Like really, really badly. And it's not getting better. And it's embarrassing, and I don't know what to do about it." My doctor stepped back into the room, shut the door, stared thoughtfully into space for all of five seconds, and said, "Painful sex usually means you were either molested as a child or have herpes. I'll get a nurse to come in and take a blood sample." And with that, she left the room before I could ask any follow-up questions, leaving me to wonder which side of that devil's coin toss I'd rather land on. I was almost disappointed when my STD panel came back clean a week later. Had I really been molested in my youth? I remember seriously disliking an elementary school gym teacher named Mr. Meehan, but I thought that had more to do with how I'd been grossly out of shape and he'd made me run laps, not because he was diddling me. I was almost positive there was no way I had been abused, but wanting to cover all my bases, I called my mom to double-check.

"Mom, this is going to sound bizarre, and try not to read too much into this, but was I ever sexually assaulted as a child?"

"Not to my knowledge," she answered in a casual, upbeat tone, as if I had just asked, "Mom, do we have a food processor?"

"Hmm," I said suspiciously.

"Why? Do you think you were?"

"No."

"Well, there's your answer. Hold on, the cat wants to say hi. EVIE, MEOW AT MEGHAN!"

So, I didn't have herpes and I wasn't molested, but something was still wrong...*down there*. I had a sex drive and I could climax when masturbating, but intercourse was physically out of the question. Even if my partner could successfully enter me, the pain was too much to bear. Over the next few months, I went to three more doctors looking for answers and was met with the same level of disinterest and condescension.

"You just need to relax more, sweetheart," said a male urologist with the largest crucifix dangling from the gaudiest gold chain resting in the thickest mane of salt-and-pepper chest hair I had ever seen. "Try taking a relaxing bath before bed, or maybe listen to some soothing music while you fall asleep. I think you'll be surprised how much better things will get if you just allow yourself loosen up a little."

I was livid. As if the answer to all of my problems was to take my vagina out to a nice wine bar, get her back to my place, light a few Yankee candles and turn on some Sade. As if it was that easy. Plus, I wasn't a high-strung individual at all. At that point in life, my lungs were comprised mostly of THC and nap cells. If I got any more relaxed, I'd risk organ failure. I left the urologist's office feeling ashamed of my body and furious; it was the last time I'd talk about my problem to anyone, let alone a doctor.

For the next five years, I fell into a pattern: I abstained from sex for as long as possible until the lack of intimacy and sexual contact became unbearable, at which point I would anesthetize myself with anything—booze, pot, coke, pills, usually a combination of any or all of the above—and have a one-night stand to satiate myself for the next six months. It didn't matter who I had sex with, but as had happened my first time with Dan, my partner would usually end up giving up and jerking off onto one of my many exciting body parts. I still felt defeated, but those first few moments of human contact, of kissing, of being held, of feeling wanted and important were worth the excruciating pain.

Sex was an integral part of not only our culture, but also of human experience, and it was an experience I couldn't relate to. While women were once taught that sex was not something to be enjoyed, but rather a necessary part of our womanly duty to procreate, we were now taught that we should love sex and openly talk about how wonderful it was over cosmos with our girlfriends. As someone who couldn't enjoy sex, I wasn't part of that conversation, which meant I had few chances to talk about how sex really was for me. Whenever the subject of conversation turned to sex, I felt like an outsider. A freak. Happy hours with my girlfriends felt like the scene in *The 40-Year Old Virgin,* when Steve Carrell's character compared grabbing a boob to grabbing a bag of sand. I tried to involve myself in sex conversations with friends to mixed results: "Yeah, man, sex. Sex is the greatest. The best thing about sex is when the guy puts his thing in and it *doesn't* feel like someone's raping you with a giant chimney sweep, you know? God, that's the best." I was too embarrassed to tell them the truth. I was already everybody's token Weird Friend; did I really have to be the one with a dysfunctional vagina too?

Every now and then I'd meet a guy I felt a connection with, but I wouldn't let it go anywhere. Interacting with the opposite sex was already hard enough without the added burden of working "SO, MY COOTER'S BROKEN!" into conversation. I became a pro at delaying dates and inventing reasons to be out of town every weekend until my potential date would give up on me, a moment I met with a mixture of relief and sadness—relief that I could stop lying, and sadness thinking about what I had lost. I felt trapped in a chastity belt made of stubborn muscle and lactic acid with nobody who could work the lock. I smoked pot, masturbated constantly, and tried to come to terms with the fact that I was going to be alone forever.

I was lying in bed taking a rare break from smoking pot and masturbating when I turned on the TV and caught an episode of MTV's *True Life*. *True Life* was a recurring MTV special that followed three unique people and focused on their everyday situations, documenting the problems they faced and goals they aspired to. In the early days of *True Life,* when MTV still had Serena Altschul and some semblance of journalistic integrity, episodes focused on serious matters like addiction, AIDS, and homelessness. 150 episodes later, MTV had clearly run out of ideas and was scraping the bottom of the creativity barrel with episodes like, "True Life: I Hate My Hair", "True Life: I Can't Control My Pet", and "True Life: I'm Having Trouble Cracking This Crab Leg Open". The episode I happened to turn on that night, however, was "True Life: I Can't Have Sex".

The episode followed three twenty-something females, Tess, Tali, and Tamara, as they struggled to come to terms with the toll the inability to have sexual intercourse had taken on each of their lives, and seek ways of treating their shared painful medical condition—vulvodynia. I couldn't believe what I had stumbled upon. It was as if I were staring into a mirror and seeing three heavily bronzed and highlighted Floridian versions of myself staring back. Each girl's experience was similar to my own, from the vaginal pain to the ignorant dismissive doctors, the depression and everything in between. For the first time in a long time, I felt less like a freak. I wasn't alone. I watched the entire episode from start to finish, found it online and watched it all over again. Only one of the girls was able to experience any pain-free sex by the end of the show, but that was more than enough hope for me. I spent hours googling 'vulvodynia', tears of relief rolling down my cheeks. It wasn't all in my head! This was not my fault! I wasn't an uptight old maid who had suppressed Mr. Meehan's sexy-recess-time advances! I had a chronic sexual pain condition affecting the vulvar area, and it had a name: vulvodynia.

As I read on, I discovered that vulvodynia was considerably

35

more common than my doctors' "YOUR HOO-HAW FEELS LIKE WHAAAA?" reactions had led me to believe, but that there was still not a lot known about it, nor was there a known cause or cure. Doctors estimated that between ten to fifteen percent of the female population suffered from vulvodynia, but believed the numbers were substantially higher when on took into account the women too embarrassed to talk about it. Their silence complicated the issue, because the less noise that was made about vulvodynia the less attention it received from the medical community, and the longer it was excluded from medical school curricula. When I read this, my heart sank: I was part of the problem. I was too embarrassed to talk about it. I had friends and family who loved and supported me unconditionally, but I couldn't bring myself to let them see this painful part of my life. Maybe it was because I saw pain as a sign of weakness, and on some level I believed having a weak vagina made me less of a woman. Maybe it was because I had low physical self-esteem and I felt embarrassed making people imagine me having sex. I *knew* I thought it made me feel less desirable to men. Sure, I had a nice rack and could recite *The Goonies* from start to finish (and hum key parts of the score on tune and with feeling), but on some deep level, I truly believed I was not worth dating if I couldn't have intercourse. I had reduced myself to a hole, and a broken one at that. But I was now ready to reach out again. After some more trawling around on the Internet, I learned there was only one doctor in the United States who specialized in vulvodynia— Dr. Andrew Goldstein—and that his office was an unbelievable five blocks from my Washington, DC apartment.

When I called Dr. Goldstein's office the next morning, I was met with good news and bad news. The good news was that they had just had a cancellation for the next afternoon, so I'd be able to skip the usual one to two month waiting period for a coveted appointment. The bad news was that an average consultation with Dr. Goldstein cost over a thousand dollars and he didn't accept insurance.

"Well, fuck me," I said to the receptionist. "Except you can't! That's the entire problem! So, fuck me all over again!"

"I know it's a lot of money," the understanding receptionist said, "but Dr. Goldstein is a *genius*. All you need is one consultation and he'll fix you. It's a one-time visit and totally worth the money." As a freelance (read: unemployed) writer, I didn't know how I was going to get the money, but the receptionist had sold me. I was already fantasizing about a miracle pill that would instantly give me glossy lips, a Farrah Fawcett blowout, and let me comfortably fuck all night with abandon. I made the appointment for the next afternoon, faxed in my new patient information, and realized that there was only one way to get a thousand dollars in one night: hooking. That was out for obvious and ironic reasons, so I'd have to go with plan B, asking my parents for the money.

I had no idea how I was going to call my mother and ask this monumental favor. Asking your parents for money when you were in your mid-twenties was degrading enough without having to specify that it was for the vagina doctor because your snatch was *six-kinds-of-broken, and gosh, what a waste*. I briefly considered lying and saying I had been arrested and needed the money for bail, but growing up in an interfaith Jewish/Catholic household had left me with an annoying inability to lie to either of my parents. I knew I'd get as far as, "Mom, I'm in j—" before thousands of years of guilt would kick in and "LIES! VAGINA FART!" would instinctively fly out of my mouth. I had to tell her the whole uncomfortable truth, and with only thirty-two dollars in my checking account and wallet full of maxed-out credit cards, I had less than twenty-four hours to do it.

Naturally, I spent the entire day procrastinating. I cleaned my apartment, I ironed a collection of shirts that had been draped over the chair in my closet for the past three years, waiting for me to make enough money to afford dry cleaning or find the energy to stand on said chair and reach the iron. I went to CVS and compared tooth whiteners, I watched a YouTube video about the history of crumping, I napped; I did everything I could do to avoid calling Diane Rowland and telling her I needed a thousand dollars to fix my broken vagina and *please, please, please don't tell Dad.*

It was getting dark outside, and my anxiety skyrocketed as I realized the window to call my mother was closing. I took a deep breath.

"I'll watch one more episode of *Toddlers & Tiaras*, and then I'll call home," I promised myself. One episode became two, two became three, and three became the long, newsy phone call to my college roommate I'd been meaning to make for months. Suddenly, it was midnight. It was late, but I knew my mom would still be up watching late-night QVC with the cat.

"Oh my god, this is ridiculous, just do it!" I yelled at myself. Riding a sudden wave of adrenalin, I stopped manically pacing around my apartment, picked up my phone, navigated to my parent's number, and hit call. My mom answered after the first ring.

"Hello?"

"Hey, it's Meg."

"Well hello, Meghan."

"Yeah. Hi. Um, sorry to call so late," I said as I popped a Xanax under my tongue to take the edge off. "I just really need to talk to you about something."

"Ok…" she said with hesitant interest.

"I need to borrow some money."

She laughed. "Well, what else is new?"

"Well, I need to borrow kind of a lot of money."

"Why?" she asked, concerned now. "What happened?"

"I don't really know how to say this to you." I was shaking. My mom let out a long, labored sigh. "Um, I just…" I trailed off. I should have waited for the Xanax to take affect before calling her. I could hear my heart pound in my ears. I was quickly approaching a full-blown panic attack.

"Spit it out, Meghan, you're killing me."

"I need help, Mom."

"Mary, mother of God—Meghan Catherine, are you pregnant?" I laughed so hard I almost choked on the now half-dissolved pill hiding under my tongue. Despite spending the majority of my adult life unable to have intercourse, I had a mother who lived in a constant state of illogical fear that her daughter was either pregnant or bulimic. She was nothing if not consistent, but that night I was grateful for the perfect segue.

"No," I said. "I wish! Actually, that's kind of the problem. I've never told you this before—I've never told anyone before—but, um, I can't have sex."

"What do you mean?" my mother asked, relieved to have dodged the grandchild bullet, but probably still wondering if I had vomited my dinner.

"It hurts too much. Sex. Sex hurts too much for me to have. It always has and it's not getting any better."

My mother was silent, so I continued.

"It's actually a pretty major part of my life, and I think about it all the time, like constantly, like it's always on my mind." I was aggressively rambling, which I always did when I got nervous. "It's embarrassing, and I can't have normal relationships, and I'm getting older and I want to get married and have kids one day, and I can't if I can't even date. I went to a few doctors years ago and they said I was either molested or have herpes and that's obviously not true, so I never said anything to anyone again about it, but there's this show on MTV—"

"Meghan, I need you to slow down." I couldn't tell if it was the Xanax kicking in or if I was just relieved to finally end the years of suffering in silence, but I completely broke down.

"Mom, I'm so fucking lonely," I managed to squeak out between huge, gasping sobs. "I just want to be normal."

"OK, sweetheart. It's OK." She was using her soothing maternal voice, reserved for special occasions and pets' deaths, which for some reason made me cry even harder. "What's the money for?"

"I found"—*sniffle*—"a specialist in the area"—*sniffle*—"and he said he could"—*sniffle*—"help me." *Hiccup*.

"How much will it cost?"

"It's like, over a thousand dollars," I said, starting to sob all over again. The guilt. It snuck up on you like that. "I'm such a fuck-up even my vagina's a fuck-up. I'm so sorry, Mom."

"When is your appointment?"

"Tomorrow afternoon."

"I'll go to the bank early tomorrow morning and put the money in your account."

My heart broke. I had spent so long feeling unlovable that this profound and selfless act of love left me feeling confused and embarrassed. I didn't know what to say. I wanted to apologize again, but I had started crying too hard to get out a coherent sentence. And then, in an even more compassionate act of love for her daughter, my mother let me cry. She didn't tell me to calm down, she didn't ask for more details or questions about when I would be able to pay the money back, she just silently stayed on the phone with me for the next hour and let me cry. My mother had been chronically sick for as long as I could remember. She suffered from fibromyalgia, hypo and then hyperthyroidism, shingles, psoriasis of the liver, diabetes, and heart disease. I knew she wasn't going to let me fight this alone. It was by no means the first time I had lain in my

ed crying about my vulvodynia, but it was the first time I had
et someone listen.

It helped. For the first time in as long as I could remember,
was convinced things were about to get better.

Norbert Weatherby

Stephanie Leone

SCAN HERE!

NORBERT WEATHERBY

Norbert Weatherby wasn't Meadowbrook's best mail-man, but he did his job. For seven years, through power outages, dangerous weather, and possible robbers at large, he did his job. Take that blizzard a few Christmases back, for example, the one that left the roads iced over for miles and people afraid of starving in front of empty cupboards. Even then, Norbert did not forgo his postal duties. Who knows how many Uncle Bobs and Aunt Cindys from Dallas, Texas had sat, hands under their wide, pillowy buttocks, anxiously wondering if the great blizzard would keep their niece Kerry-Anne in Meadowbrook, Pennsylvania from receiving their dog-decorated, "We woof! you a Merry Christmas!" card in time. Norbert Weatherby, Federal Postal Person, would never even think of allowing anything to go undelivered. Particularly not Witty Animal Holiday Cards, which he liked. Norbert Weatherby bravely tended to every single house during the blizzard, so that every Kerry-Anne had a perfect Christmas morning, with every card and parcel exactly where it was meant to be. When the people on his route thanked him, Norbert replied that he was only following instructions.

And that is true of him still. For instance, he brought the mail all the way to Mrs. Katz's doorstep at her request even though he was terrified of her vicious yard-dog, Charles Winston. Every third Thursday of the month, he held Mr. Lintner's mail in a small box in his truck until the following Monday while still delivering Mrs. Lintner's mail, because according

45

to Mr. Lintner there were some mail that was private even in marriage, and could he not mention their agreement to Mrs. Lintner, please and thank you. During the holidays, Norbert included candy canes in everyone's mail. Even the Horowitzs received a candy cane, though Norbert tied a small plastic menorah with a blue ribbon to theirs. People were grateful for Norbert's years of service. All of Meadowbrook left Norbert a little something for his time during the holidays, mostly short, handwritten, "Thanks for all your hard work. Merry Christmas and a blessed New Year!" on leftover stationery embossed in a festive red or gold ink. They were, as these things go, repetitive and practical, which, for Norbert, was thoughtful. He kept them all alphabetized and displayed on his dining room table upon receiving them, and took them down to his basement on December 26th, on which day they were filed in a box labeled Holiday Cards from (Year).

Every morning, Norbert woke up at 05:15 to have his hazelnut coffee and read *The Bucks County Daily.* He liked reading the obituaries and doing crossword puzzles, both for their systematic natures, and if he started by 05:30 he had just enough time to complete half of one (less on days when a particular clue truly stumped him as he could only attempt to solve clue number seven after he'd solved clue number six, and so on) before he had to leave. His mail route was often far more exciting than the puzzles anyway. Such as when old Ms. Wilkinson was found eight-days dead only when a neighbor finally smelled rotting flesh and happened to catch Norbert who was passing through. Or when Father Bowen, the local pastor, had passed away so quietly and peacefully that no one noticed until he failed to show up to lead the 10:30 Sunday mass.

Twice a month on Tuesdays, when he got paid, Norbert would get up at 05:00 so that he could stop at the bank next to the post office to deposit his check before his shift began.

Niqueria, whose mail truck was parked next to his, greeted him with the same, "Hey, how's the weather gonna be today, Weatherby? Ha ha," to which Norbert would reply, "Why, I'm sure it'll be quite nice, Niqueria." Niqueria always made that same joke, which Norbert didn't find funny, but appreciated she made anyway. Every day.

This particular morning was a Tuesday, but not a payday, so Norbert woke up at the usual 05:15. Though he could normally tell by the temperature of his coffee how much longer he had for the paper, Norbert checked the large wall clock anyway, and checked that against his Snoopy watch, which his mother, Mrs. Nora Weatherby, had presented to him at his high school graduation. He still watched Peanuts on his VHS player because of the old commercials: a talking baby doll followed by paper towels followed by Oscar Meyer Hot Dogs, then back to Charlie Brown and Snoopy. As a child, Mrs. Nora Weatherby used to make him Oscar Meyer Hot Dogs with a side of Macaroni and Cheese and frozen peas once a week after he'd seen that commercial with the brother and sister, tired from soccer practice, refueling with their Oscar Meyer Hot Dogs. Norbert had never been an athletic child, but he'd wanted to be. Occasionally, Grown-Up Norbert would make Oscar Meyer Hot Dogs for himself, but it never tasted the same as when his mother had made them, assuring him that his bones and muscles would grow strong if he ate the ideal portions of protein, carbohydrates and vegetables every day. He still measured out his portions on the special plate Mrs. Nora Weatherby had insisted he take when he moved into his house. With its three different-sized sections, Norbert always knew he was eating well, though the Oscar Meyer Hot Dogs stretched slightly beyond the edges of the allocated protein section. His stomach draped over the waistband of his pants, which had tightened over the years, but that was due to lack of exercise rather than his eating habits, which were as perfect

47

as his mother had made them, with the exception of the occasional bag of chips at night.

Norbert's delivery route was simple. He covered the houses for five different neighborhoods, all separated by tree-lined, bird-filled streets, which would soon be devastatingly bare. Fallen leaves made a pleasant crunching noise whenever he turned a corner slowly, which was every time as the speed limit was fifteen or twenty miles per hour in his neighborhoods, but he would have slowed down anyway to listen to the dead leaves die again. They were a nice checkpoint, a sound indicating another job completed, a point of his work he'd come to expect. Sometimes, the tones they made were different, and they sounded like a song to Norbert. He imagined these leaves as the opening soundtrack to the movie about his life, with quick cuts to all the different mailboxes he served, their various shapes and colors a perfect background mosaic for the credits. Inside his mail truck, he had a box containing thirty alphabetized CDs, which he rarely touched. He played only one song during the whole of his three hour route: *My Way* by Frank Sinatra. It was the song which best accompanied the tones of the crunching leaves. He liked thinking that he had "traveled each and every highway" as a mail carrier; he found it quite satisfying to be reminded of such as he rode along the suburban roads carrying important correspondences in tow.

The first street on his route offered few revealing pieces of mail for its occupants. A postcard from Jennifer in Hawaii who had gotten a bad sunburn but was having a great vacation to Kathleen O'Brien at 1633 Stockton Road. Mr. Whilely at 1636 was likely late on his electric bill based on the *FINAL NOTICE!* stamped across the envelope addressed to him, which was no different than the envelope Norbert had delivered to him last month and the month before that. The Horowitzs had an envelope from Our Lady Help of Christians Catholic Parish, which, upon further inspection, revealed a second envelope for collections. For Mr. Lintner, a small, cream-colored envelope made from quality paper grain with lovely script on the front, which Norbert tucked between a few bills and a letter from the public library lest Mrs. Lintner notice the feminine handwriting that did not belong to Mr. Lintner's mother, sister, or cousin Betty. They were the three other women in his life besides his wife and their cat, Genevieve. At the McNally mailbox, the leaves continued to crunch even after he braked. Before him, on the ever so slightly inclined lawn, two children ran thrashing through piles of raked, dead leaves, kicking and tossing them into the air to scatter that which was orderly. Norbert dragged his fingers through his thinning hair, tucking a stray lock into his gelled clump of mousy gray. The children should leave the leaves alone. He recalled the way his mother would meticulously color arrange yellows with yellows, reds with reds, until she had made three plump piles of leaves, for which Norbert would wait all afternoon to ruin. He didn't want to ruin them anymore. How nice it would be if the leaves would only fall now where he wanted them to. If they could arrange themselves by color into fluffy piles. He pushed gently on the gas pedal, silently singing along with Sinatra, the McNallys' junk mail still in his lap. *And more, much more than this, I did it my way.*

There was a pale yellow envelope addressed to Alfred J. Perkins at 1650 Stockton. Alfred J. Perkins was the son of Wilfred Ignatius Perkins of the Perkins Pennsylvania Pickle Company, which produced some of the finest pickles Norbert, and most of Pennsylvania, had ever eaten. Perkins Pennsylvania Pickle Company pickles were Produced With Care in Erie, Pennsylvania according to the label on their jars. Erie was far from Meadowbrook, but Alfred J. Perkins had purchased a house located on Norbert's route after Wilfred Ignatius Perkins passed away. Meadowbrook had barely contained its excitement upon the arrival of the new celebrity.

There had even been talk of pickle discounts for all the local grocery stores and delis. Delivering to a local celebrity held great responsibility. Norbert stacked all of Alfred J. Perkins' mail expertly, fashioning them into a delicate bulk with special rubber bands, which he strategically placed in the mailbox without bending a single thing.

Norbert had only seen Alfred J. Perkins once, when he'd parked his truck in order to deliver the mail to Alfred's door instead of just leaving it in the mailbox like usual. It had been a particularly heavy batch of letters, all stamped with the Perkins Pennsylvania Pickle Company emblem, and it was raining on top of that. Alfred had answered the door in a fluffy pink bathrobe that cushioned the sagging skin of his neck and hung from his thin frame. His head, Norbert had thought, seemed perched there, ready to snap or take flight if Alfred was startled. Whether it was because Norbert had caught him in soft loungewear or for something else, Alfred had not taken kindly to his gesture, his hands quick to find a nearby gold trophy to hurl at Norbert. He had not attempt to interact with Alfred J. Perkins again.

Norbert turned the envelope over in his hands. A flower Forever Stamp decorated the appropriate upper right-hand corner, and the pale outline of a pickle was barely visible on the worn surface. Alfred J. Perkins, Norbert knew, no longer resided at 1650 Stockton as he was six months dead. Norbert hadn't solved a single crossword clue on the day he'd read the news of Alfred J, Perkins' death, but had adjusted his schedule to go to the grocery store before work to purchase a jar of Perkins Pennsylvania Pickle Company pickles out of respect. Alfred J. Perkins had been a great man.

The grain of the paper did not betray its contents when held up to sunlight, so Norbert tucked the letter away and kept driving, letting Frank's voice fill up the quiet spaces of his afternoon, save for the leaves crunching under his quickening turns.

After successfully delivering to all five neighborhoods, Norbert returned to his desk inside the post office for the remaining hours of the work day. It wasn't unusual for him to be quiet, and the manager, Mr. Lionsgaton, was far too busy trying to get Linda the secretary to go to Blitzed Billiard Night with him at the local pool hall to notice anything out of the ordinary. Alfred J. Perkins's letter was now tucked into the waistband of Norbert's underwear. At 16:45, Norbert pushed his chair back from his desk, stood up, and said, "Mr. Lionsgaton, I forgot to pick up cat food for Rocky, my cat, and I have to drive out to Philadelphia later tonight to see my uncle. He's not awful, but he does have permanent brain damage from his motorcycle accident a few years back, and Tuesday is my day to watch him. Normally, I would have picked up some cat food on my shopping day, which is Friday, and, well, I would really appreciate leaving fifteen minutes early, if that's okay with you."

No one stopped typing, filing, coffee-sipping, or under-the-desk-thigh-squeezing when Norbert stood up. Mr. Lionsgaton leaned back against Linda's desk while still working hard to bend the paperclip he was holding into a wiry heart. Blitzed Billiard Night was hours away.

"Sure, no problem, Weatherby. See you tomorrow."

"Thank you, Mr. Lionsgaton," Norbert said, already halfway through the office. He hoped his real uncle would not fall ill in the meantime.

"I didn't know Norbert had a cat," said Linda.

"Me neither," said Mr. Lionsgaton. "But I'd love to talk about it with some beer and pool sticks."

"I *bet* you would," said Linda.

***

Norbert did not stop at the stop signs on his way home for more than a few seconds. He didn't take the longer route home, which allowed him to listen to *My Way* five times instead of two and a half, and he didn't back up into his driveway as he usually did. Instead, he pulled in rather crookedly. Had his house and car keys not been attached to the same ring, he would not have realized that he'd left the engine running. The front yard, he knew, needed to be raked, particularly the great piles of red, gold, and orange leaves that he'd just organized yesterday. They were now a hopeless mess, sloppier and uglier under the darkening sky.

Sitting down at his kitchen table, Norbert at last slowed his pace, breathing heavily. His left hand tapped a rhythm against the surface. The letter was wrinkled with sweat when he pulled it from his waistband, and it curled against the table. He wished he had time to put a weight on it, to smooth it out again. A butter knife would do the trick; his mother never let him have anything sharper than that around the house.

> *Dear Mr. Perkins,*
> *I hope this letter finds you well and that this heat has not been too much for you this summer (I myself am perspiring uncontrollably, and I'm afraid my petunias are suffering for it!). I write in regards to some of the matters we discussed at our last meeting, for which we absolutely need to schedule a follow-up. I am free most days, except Sunday, from now through September. Please let me know what works best for you in the manner that we previously discussed.*
> *Looking forward,*
> *Anabelle*
> *P.S. I finally had a pickle-back. You were right!*

Norbert read the letter several times before noticing that it, too, had a pickle illustration imprinted behind the text. Anabelle had dated the letter August of the current year, suggesting that she did not read *The Bucks County Daily*, since Alfred J. Perkins had been very much dead by the date of her letter. She had to have corresponded regularly and recently with him to write Alfred so casually. The envelope was postmarked a few days ago from Erie, but the return address did not include a house number. Norbert found the system behind addressing, sending and receiving letters so manageable, and he couldn't understand why someone would send a letter with an improperly-written return address. Poor Mr. Perkins. He would never read the letter. Norbert realized he'd been holding his breath. He began inhaling for five counts, exhaling for five more. He'd been preparing his entire postal career for this: a letter with no forwarding address that needed to be returned. Norbert Weatherby, Federal Postal Person, had a federal job to do.

He refolded the letter into its envelope and placed it in a Ziploc bag. According to Federal Postal Law, Rule 32C, Section 5.53, mail was Private Property, only to be opened by the person to whom it was addressed. Norbert knew this rule and all the other Federal Postal Laws, by heart. But Rule 45C, Section 1: Deceased Person's Mail stated that, "If one shares an address with someone who has since died and would normally receive their mail, one is entitled to open and manage the deceased's mail." Norbert had not technically shared an address with Alfred J. Perkins, but since his house was uninhabited, Norbert had no choice but to *manage* the mail. He would explain all of this to Anabelle when he found her, who would not mind that he had opened the letter, he was sure. She would be too overwhelmed by how well he'd done his job.

At the bottom of the stairs to the basement was a fishing box, which Norbert brought up to his kitchen table and opened to refresh his memory of its contents: a flashlight, dried packs of ramen noodles, an empty thermos, batteries, paperclips, a spare butter knife (almost as good as a pocket-knife), pink ribbon, an old copy of Dr. Seuss' *Oh, The Places You'll Go!*, a map of the United States and of Pennsylvania, utensils, a blue pen, and a book of crossword puzzles, unused. Norbert had never been fishing and didn't think he'd ever go, but the utilitarian look of it seemed perfect for a Federal Post Office Emergency Box. He tucked the letter in the top compartment so it wouldn't bend. He would take his winter coat, a simple black wool thing, inside of which he had sewn several extra pockets in case of a situation like this, as an extra precaution. The extra pockets looked more official than those of his nicest sport coats. Norbert surveyed his appearance before the full-length mirror, nodding solemnly. His Federal Postal name tag was pinned over his chest just so. He was ready.

Finally, a chance to show the world what being a mail carrier was all about. Norbert could barely buckle his seatbelt. "Just doing my job," he would say. It would extend for two pages in *The Bucks County Daily*: "Out of A Pickle! Local Postal Hero Returns Letter To Family of Late Alfred Perkins." The Meadowbrook Post Office would become top-rated and secretly aid the FBI in cracking cases where clues could be found in mail. Norbert Weatherby, FBI and Postal Expert. He started the engine, turning up the volume on the stereo so that the seats vibrated a little. Here was a real mystery, landing in his lap as easily as Mr. Lionsgaton's creeping hand up Linda's thighs. And a woman named Anabelle. Clearly, Alfred had found her important enough to have specific, planned methods of communication, yet she did not know he had died, or knew he had died but sent him a letter anyway. The possibilities were endless. His whole mail-carrying career, Norbert was certain, depended upon this moment. And pickles. He would have pickles to last him a lifetime. He'd donate them to Meadowbrook and all its grocery stores. He'd keep half the jars for himself and then distribute them evenly around Meadowbrook starting with Babo Café and ending with Zumba+, a place in and out of which Norbert frequently noticed beautiful women gliding.

Norbert felt that most women glided like that. His mother had, he was certain, but hers had been a different kind of gliding. He would have to find a woman who glided the way his mother had. Norbert knew all about women from the magazines he delivered. He knew that there were certain things they liked, like shoulders to cry on that were attached to strong arms. Thankfully, carrying the mail for so long had given Norbert superior upper-body strength. He still couldn't manage more than five pushups, but it would come with time. (He skipped the pages about "Women in the Bedroom" because, as Mrs. Nora Weatherby had told him, he would know what to do because everyone did. And Mrs. Nora Weatherby had never been wrong about anything.)

He could see the headlines now: "Local Mail Carrier/Legendary Perkins Pickle Hero To Wed." People would approach him on the job while he was buying milk: "Please, Mrs. Delilah, you know I can't share my fiancée's cheesecake recipe with you *before* the wedding. Yes she *is* very pretty, thank you, Mrs. Delilah. By the way, I have a nice card arriving for you in the mail, Mrs. Delilah, it *might* be an invitation of sorts, but I won't spoil it for you."

She, his Zumba+ fit fiancée, would come into the Meadowbrook Post Office to bring him lunch. They would eat Oscar Meyer Hot Dogs together and watch his old Peanuts VHS tapes. She would laugh when he mouthed the words to all the lines. Sitting on the couch all perfect, he'd kiss her forehead right in front of Snoopy in his little red doghouse. She'd make him take off his clothes because of all the energy expended in her Zumba+ class, and he would, as his mother had promised, know exactly what to do.

He was hungry. What if the Erie Post Office didn't even recognize Prickly Pine Lane as a street of residence, when really it was? Anabelle had been waiting for a response for months now, wondering about Alfred J. Perkins and their abandoned discussion topics. Norbert could relieve her frantic questioning. He hadn't considered that he might be conveying the news of Alfred J. Perkins' death to the entire town. Erie could be backward, without much television access. Perhaps they'd turned against Perkins Pennsylvania Pickle Company pickles when Alfred moved. He pulled over into the parking lot of an establishment called Erie's, which looked to be open based on the neon signage and the few other cars in the lot.

He stepped out of the truck and brushed his wool coat off. Buttoned up, it made Norbert look as though he occupied an official position. He walked around to the other side of the truck, enjoying the way the coat kept everything tightly in place as he moved. The fishing box, strapped to the passenger seat, contained some fake, bushy eyebrows on plastic posts that could clip onto any pair of glasses, which Norbert had once used as part of a Halloween costume for a party, except he hadn't exactly been invited to it, so he had driven around his neighborhood with them instead, a bowl of candy in his lap to give to Trick-Or-Treaters. He'd returned home that night with his candy still very much untouched. Mothers had hurried away at the sight of his slow-moving truck, pulling their costumed children with them. Perhaps he could wear them now in case he made the evening news. His first time on television should be as memorable as possible, and the eyebrows made him look bold. Norbert had read in a magazine in the waiting room of his last doctor's appointment that women liked men with well-groomed eyebrows because it meant that they knew how to take care of themselves. He checked his reflection in the mirror of the car. The copy of *Oh, The Places You'll Go!* was in the box keeping the letter flat and protected. He thought, just this once, of calling himself another name— perhaps Norbert Seussaby—to match the nature of his new, exotic mission. He exited the car and made his way to the diner door, jumping slightly at the tiny *bing!* of an attached bell that alerted people of their comings and goings.

There was a counter at which a few people sat on high swivel stools. The wall behind it hosted a variety of dishware, all of different sets. Norbert counted seven different coffee mugs on the shelf behind the cash register alone. *Don't Talk To Me Until This Is Empty* said one, while another had a crude graphic of a woman's torso. The man behind the counter had not acknowledged Norbert, though he was not busy doing anything else. Norbert situated himself onto one of the stools, his foot slipping a little so that he had to slam his hand down on the counter for balance. It was hard to sit in his coat; it was tighter than the last time he'd worn it.

"Good evening, sir. I am Norbert Seussaby, and I'd like to order the best thing on your menu from the breakfast section. I've been driving a long time, and I'm starved. I particularly like Perkins Pennsylvania Pickle Company pickles if you have them, but if you don't that's okay."

The man behind the counter did not look up at him as he was busy preparing a fresh pot of coffee. A teenage boy dressed in black, and an older man polishing off what looked as though it might once have been a very ketchup-covered burger also sat at the counter. Norbert had never been to a diner before, because Mrs. Nora Weatherby had always told him they were dirty. There was a jukebox in the corner by a bathroom sign that said, *Ask for the key if you paid.*

"You from up north?" the man behind the counter asked with a grunt. His thick-rimmed glasses were filthy with grease. Did many women approach him for those? Norbert would have to ask. He couldn't tell if he looked smart or dirty.

"Yes. From far away." Norbert noticed for the first time the seventeen-inch tall menu before him. A sticky smear kept the edges of two of the pages together, from years of dirty fingers, no doubt. He took a tissue from his pocket and wiped it down.

"You from Philly or somethin'?"

"Why yes, I am. Right from the city. I'm Norbert. Norbert Seussaby."

"Seussaby?"

"Yes. Seussaby." Norbert enjoyed that at least his disguised name was getting attention. The women would like it! Pleased that he had come up with it so quickly, he continued. "It's a strange name, I know, but—"

"No, it's just that your name tag says Norbert Weatherby," the man said, his bored tone unchanged.

"Oh." Norbert deflated immediately. "Yes, I just wanted to try it out, I guess. Spice things up a little. Well not 'spice,' more like 'Seuss'! Ha ha!"

"Uh huh."

"I'm looking for a woman by the name of Anabelle, who lives on Prickly Pine Lane. I have to return a letter that she tried to send to a now-dead inhabitant of a house on my mail route. I'm a Federal Post Officer," Norbert said importantly.

"She lives in the wooden house, second to last on the street. Take a left out of here and follow the road for a little. Take another left at the first street you see, and then a quick right. Now what can I get you?" the man asked, though it didn't sound as if he really wanted to know.

"Oh, I'll just take a donut to go, thank you," Norbert said, excited to find Anabelle.

"I thought you said you were starving."

"No, a donut will do just fine, thank you. Do you have a bathroom I could use?" Norbert stood up, pulling down the lapels of his coat and letting his hands linger on them.

"Bathroom is for seated customers only." The man shoved a paper bag to him. "Come again."

***

58

Norbert wiped off his hands after carefully eating his donut. Dessert for dinner tasted wonderful. Mrs. Nora Weatherby would never have let him have a donut until he'd eaten at least half of his Oscar Meyer Hot Dog. He would tell the news channel that he'd been so keen on finding Anabelle he hadn't even had a proper dinner. What a champ, what a hero! He got back into his car and drove along happily, repeating the lines of Anabelle's letter in his head and picturing his face on TV. Left, left again, quick right. The houses were spaced further and further apart as he continued down Prickly Pine Lane. Most were modest, with simple mailboxes and a tree or two on the front lawn. One driveway even had a basketball hoop. What if he and Anabelle had a son who became a basketball star? "He definitely got *that* from his mother," Norbert would joke at dinner parties. "Not from me. His nerve he gets from me." Their son would be famous too, but they would keep Norbert's house in Meadowbrook, which everyone would think was just so great. "They can afford so much more with that famous basketball son of theirs, but they live so simply," they would say. "That Norbert Weatherby is a stand-up guy."

There was no mistaking Anabelle's house at the end of the street, which was indeed made almost entirely out of wood. The sizeable front window emitted a golden glow that cast a beautiful light on the fallen leaves. Norbert almost didn't mind that they weren't in organized piles. The remains of Anabelle's summer petunias had shed dried petals on the lawn.

He took the letter from the box and headed to the front door. His coat and glasses were in place, though he'd missed a few dabs of pink frosting from the donut in the corners of his mouth. The doorbell echoed loudly.

He heard the unlatching of several locks and the door opened a crack.

"Uh, hi, can I help you?"

She was far younger than he had expected, probably only

twenty or twenty-one, with dark shiny hair. From the little o
her face that peaked out from inside, Norbert could see tha
she was wearing glasses. He was glad he had chosen to wea
his, though he supposed he would eventually have to tell he
that the eyebrows attached to them weren't real.

"Hello, my name is Norbert Weatherby. I'm a Federal Pos
Officer from Meadowbrook, here to return a letter sent from
this address."

She didn't open the door wider. Why wasn't she opening
the door?

"Uh, okay…? It's kind of late to be returning a letter."

"Oh, but it'll only take a minute!" Norbert exclaimed, his
voice high-pitched. "It really is an important letter. You see
I tried to deliver it today, but the person to whom it was addressed, whom I think you'll realize is very important, is actually…well, he won't ever receive the letter, so legally I have
to return it to the sender, which is you, but you didn't put a
full return address on it so I had to come bring it to you. And
in the letter, which I only read because Rule 45C, Section 1
states that if…well, couldn't I just come in?"

She still did not widen the door, though Norbert could see
her slipper-covered feet peeking out from some striped paja-
ma pants. Mrs. Nora Weatherby had told him that a woman
should never answer the door in her bedclothes. He would
talk to Anabelle about it after he presented the letter.

"I really don't know what you're talking about, but it's su-
per late and I'm not down with this—"

"Babe, is everything all right? Who are you talking to?"

A male voice. Heat rose to Norbert's face, the way it had
when he'd once sifted through Mr. Lintner's magazines and
found pictures of a fully naked woman, posed in a way that
scared him. He'd closed it abruptly, but then opened it again
to view the oily body that looked nothing like any of the wom-
en he knew at work. He thought about that naked woman of-

ten, but never flipped through one of Mr. Lintner's magazines again.

"Some guy returning a letter."

"So late?" The voice was getting louder. Footsteps. Oh dear.

"Yeah, that's what I told him? I guess we can take it."

Norbert tried doing his deep breathing exercises, in for five, out for five, but it was very hard. He was shivering and hot, and now that he'd thought of the naked woman, he couldn't get her out of his head and focus on his job.

The door opened all the way and a man stepped out from behind Anabelle. He was tall and muscled, not in the way Mr. Lionsgaton was, but like the arms of the boys who'd always aimed for his glasses during games of high school dodge ball. He had a thick, full head of hair and was not wearing glasses. Norbert was suddenly keenly aware of his own baldness.

"What do you want?"

Norbert wondered if his own voice sounded that deep. "S-sorry, I realize it's late, but I just really need to return this to Anabelle and tell her something important." He was glad he'd put the letter in a Ziploc bag. His hands were sweating all over it.

"Anabelle? Anabelle is my mom." The girl shifted her weight onto her hip and crossed her arms, looking at Norbert the way his schoolteachers had when he'd said something wrong. The bathrobe was thin, and Norbert could see the outline of her figure perfectly, parts of it as clearly as though the bathrobe was not there at all. "What do you want with her?"

"Oh, there's been a great misunderstanding!" What a relief! This was *not* Anabelle! Though he did think this girl's figure looked very nice. "I thought you were Anabelle. She addressed this letter to a man named, well." He dropped his voice lower, slowing down as he said, "To Mr. Alfred J. Perkins."

61

"Ugh, that old weirdo? He died, like, forever ago." The girl was tapping her foot now; the man's hand circled her waist. He was moving his thumb up and down by her hipbone, slowly moving his hand to her backside. Norbert's eyes tracked the motion. It was a nice thing to touch someone else in front of a complete stranger.

"You—you know about Mr. Perkins?"

"Yeah. My mom worked for him for like, ever. He was so lame."

Norbert felt like a balloon whose air had been let out. He had never felt this way before. Was his stomach upset maybe from having dessert for dinner? "Well, technically, I need to return this letter to Anabelle, who is your mother, correct?"

The girl blinked.

"Yeah, I just told you that. She's not home, though, so you can't. It's just us tonight." She smiled up at the man, who looked even bigger and more muscular now. Witnessing such a look, Norbert recalled what Mrs. Nora Weatherby had said, that he would know what to do. He wondered if she was right. He wished the look had been directed at him.

"Well, I don't think I can leave the letter with you. It's against Rule, uh, 32B section 9 of the Federal Postal Law." This was not a rule, Norbert knew, but he couldn't leave yet.

She laughed, but not as if she thought he had made a joke. It wasn't a good laugh.

"Whatever, dude. Why don't you just wait outside on the porch? She'll be home soon."

"Oh!" Norbert smiled, relieved. "Oh! Yes, yes of course. I'll wait for Anabelle. Thank you!" The girl closed the door in his face. From the front window, Norbert could see her and the man walking, intertwined, with the man's hand across her backside.

Norbert made his way onto the porch and sat on the step, admiring night for the first time in a while. In Meadowbrook, he didn't leave the house after dinner, partly because he was scared, partly because he didn't have a reason to. The night smelled different here. He pretended he was in a quiet contest with the great outdoors, but he began tapping his foot, drumming his thumbs. His mind was so occupied he was sure it translated to real noise. He had to deliver the letter, Anabelle or not. He had a job to do. And Anabelle would appreciate his dutiful gesture. He'd delivered under worse conditions before, like the blizzard a few Christmases back. Anabelle would tell her daughter and her daughter's boyfriend to get lost and then ask if he'd like to take a bath with her. He'd try to talk about the letter, but she'd shush him and say they could talk about that later. He stood up, took a deep breath, and knocked several times at the door, hard.

No one answered, but the door was unlocked. He could always just wait in the living room. The first meeting with Anabelle couldn't be on her porch.

Anabelle's house was modestly decorated with salm-on-colored carpeting and lots of side tables. The first one Norbert saw had geraniums in a vase that were starting to dry out. A tiny pile of dead petals littered the floor. How often did she clean? He always swept before and after dinner. Now he could prepare for Anabelle, maybe study her a little. He could look at her family photos or the type of mail she received. A standing frame on the coffee table in the living room caught his eye. He moved toward it, trying to ignore the number of used dishes left out in the kitchen (eight, plus a cutting board, which didn't exactly count.) In the frame was a beautiful woman with graying brown hair and a burgundy sweater like one that Mrs. Nora Weatherby had worn. She was smiling, revealing a small space between her front teeth that Norbert instantly loved. This had to be Anabelle. Next to her was a man with a familiar face, who was holding a certificate, though he was not smiling as big as she.

On the wall above the fireplace, which was very dusty, were more family photos, including some with Anabelle's daughter, looking much younger than now. Norbert thought of her bathrobe again, blushing. He adjusted the waistband of his pants, which had been tightening uncomfortably ever since he'd arrived. There was a framed paper next to the photos: *Certificate of Excellence for Excellent Public Relations for the Perkins Pennsylvania Pickle Company*.

Looking back at the photograph of a smiling Anabelle, Norbert wondered how he hadn't noticed Alfred J. Perkins before. Anabelle worked for him, of course! This is why they had had correspondence. They had to be close if she had a photo of him in her living room. She'd be so glad about the letter, it could have been their last correspondence *ever*, and now she could frame it along with her certificate. He pictured a photo of himself and Anabelle next to the one of her and Alfred, its frame slightly bigger than all the others.

There was a sound from nearby. A thumping that was growing louder, a steady squeaking. The floor could cave with thumping like that. Norbert stood up and walked cautiously to the door across from the living room. It sounded as if something terrible was happening. Norbert wondered if the man could be hurting Anabelle's daughter. He gulped, walked to the door, and knocked twice, pressing his ear to it.

"Hello? Is everything all right in there?"

He couldn't pinpoint exactly what he was hearing. The thumping and squeaking were loud; he couldn't hear voices. They could also be jumping on the bed, he reasoned, pressing his ear harder against the door.

"Oh…*oh* yes, Brett, *yes*." The girl's voice sounded lower than what Norbert had been introduced to, and it caused an odd tingling in his groin. He raised his fist to knock again when he heard moaning. It made his mind fuzzy. He should be learning more about Anabelle, but he found himself sinking to the floor, listening intently to the sounds. His pants were tightening uncomfortably again. Maybe he could unzip them for a while. He thought of the bathrobe and of the shape of her chest beneath it. He thought of the naked woman in Mr. Lintner's magazine, of Anabelle, oily and in a bathtub. His head was a freight train of pictures that quickened in his panic and enjoyment. His hand moved into his pants. He put his other hand on the door behind him for support and closed his eyes. A high, odd noise escaped him again and again.

"What in *God's* name do you think you are *doing!*"

Norbert took his hand, now wet and sticky, from his crotch, and snapped his head around. Anabelle stood before him, but she was not smiling as she had been in the picture in the living room. Her beautiful bottom lip was curled inward as if she were about to spit fire, and her hair was coming out of its ponytail. Norbert had never been so awestruck and frightened by a woman in his life. A few cracked eggs from her dropped grocery bags ran along the hardwood floor to kiss the tips of his feet, sprawled out in front of him like a rag doll's.

The door swung open behind him, revealing her daughter and the girl's boyfriend, both sweaty and wearing towels. The girl screamed like her mother when she laid eyes on Norbert.

"Oh my god! Ew!"

"Who is this man and why—In my *living room!*" Anabelle was turning purple now.

"Oh my god, Mom, I don't know, we told him to wait outside because he said he had a letter for you. I didn't know he was, like, a pedophile or something. *Ew!*"

Norbert could only hold his limp penis in his hand in indescribable shame. This was not how it was supposed to happen. Somehow, during the moment, he'd decided to use the Ziploc bag with the letter as a napkin to clean the mess off his hand. The letter! His mission!

"Are you Anabelle? I have a letter for you from Alfred J.

Perkins. I'm Norbert Weatherby from the Federal Post Office; I came to return this to you." He barely recognized the sound of his own voice, and he couldn't decide where it had come from, the ability to speak again. He stood up, forgetting to close up his pants, and held the letter out to Anabelle.

"Get out! Get *out*! I'm calling the police, you filthy son of a bitch!" Anabelle screamed. She ran to the kitchen, grabbing her phone.

Norbert had never been screamed at like this before, but he understood he had to go. He grabbed the Ziploc bag and ran for the door, tripping and falling on the leaked eggs in the hallway, slamming his knee onto the floor. "Ow," he gasped. There were tears forming in his eyes, but Anabelle and the man were coming and so he ran again. Out the door, down the porch steps, down the driveway, into his truck. His hands were trembling so violently it took him three tries to start the engine.

"No, no, no," he sobbed, turning the key again and again. Brett and Anabelle followed him down the driveway.

"I'll catch you, you bastard! You better keep running!"

Norbert drove and drove, ignoring the speed limits for the first time in his life. Past the Erie Diner, past the beautiful trees, onto the highway. He could hear sirens behind him; he pushed the gas pedal harder. He wanted Mrs. Nora Weatherby and wished she wasn't dead. She had seen what he'd done. He was sorry, so very, very sorry for Mrs. Nora Weatherby. Sorry for Anabelle and for her daughter and the man, for all the things they'd called him, all those awful names. He cried, big ugly sobs, turning up the volume on the stereo, looking for Frank's voice. Fall, he decided was still his favorite season. It brought so much chaos, just like his job did sometimes, but there was always a way to restore order. *And more, much more than this, I did it my way.* He cried and cried some more.

He would write to Anabelle tomorrow and apologize. He

would also write to her daughter and the man and Alfred J. Perkins and to the guy behind the counter at Erie Diner and to Mr. Lionsgaton and the President of The Federal Postal Reserve. He'd offer to arrange Anabelle's leaves for her and to clean her house. He could see red and blue lights in his rearview mirror, and sped up. Anabelle would scold her daughter for how she'd treated him.

"Look at how beautifully he organized our fallen leaves! And we didn't even ask him! He's such a good man. Forget about yesterday." That's what she would say. And he would shrug it off with a laugh, saying that it was no big feat.

FRANCINE

SONIA BEYDA

SCAN HERE!

FRANCINE

In Carrara, blood was shed on the white marble like a fuckin' slaughterhouse. If you didn't clean it within five minutes, the sun dried it up and it stained as a maroon crust.

David was well-known in the quarry of white, gray veined marble. He got sold off to officials of the Florence Cathedral with intention to become one of twelve biblical statues, specifically that of David, who battled Goliath and composed the Book of Psalms. He was passed through the hands of multiple artisans until settling into Michelangelo's, who completed him. Michelangelo was said to believe that the sculpture was already in the marble and the artist need only to uncover it.

This was true: We were here—you just needed to shape us. As the decades went by, my friends and I watched the fresh marble on top get cut out into perfectly symmetrical slabs through an ancient system that got the job done with no guarantee a finger would not come off as well.

Once time passed the Middle Ages, the Renaissance, Baroque, and Romantic periods, we knew that our chance to reside in epic museums had long gone. We were buried as ancient marble, only to be dug up when the cuts reached us, and that came with time. We knew this; *I* knew this. I just didn't think sculpting marble would be a craft of the past when my time came. We might become tabletops in wealthy Italian homes, but we knew that was the lowest we'd sink given the rarity of Carrara marble. I stuck around the quarry long enough to presume to know my fate. And I knew I was leaving soon, I just didn't know where.

Giovanni handled my exit, working with precise mathematics, which some would say were not necessary when you were going on your fifty-fifth year working in Carrara, but he knew the risk didn't decrease with time. One intern slashed his hand open and splattered blood all over me. I'd never felt moisture before and it was quite invigorating. They wrapped me, and I said goodbye to Carrara, my home.

The transit was long. I was exposed to accents and languages I had never heard before, and it made me wonder where my new home would be. I prepared myself for China. I prepared myself to be made into a million kitsch trinkets for a gift shop. Then I stopped imagining because I remembered what Michelangelo said: Whatever I became has been in me, in my fate, since my birth. It was time for my revelation. It was time for me to take on my true form.

My protective wrappings were ripped off by a naked woman, who giggled in delight. A man with a brownish gray beard ran over with a small white towel covering his bottom, and pulled her away from me aggressively. Her face dropped as she caught her balance and quickly ran to the far end of the room near the windows to gather her stuff. She returned, fully dressed in a silver low-cut gown and turned to the man who was still undoing the mess she had made of my wrapping. He looked at her and sighed apologetically.

"I'm sorry I pushed you. I think it's smart that you go," he said.

His stare was poised and strong, and he spoke with no doubt. His voice was deep and raspy. His presence was mysterious and I was in awe of him.

"You're a dick, Moe," she said as she stormed into the bathroom, slamming the door shut behind her. "If I leave now, I'm not coming back…No. No, I'm not. Five years and I can't see what you work on? Five years and you won't even let me touch your dumb marble? What am I to you?"

The voice became distant. But I heard wet sobs and a dripping nose.

"...kids, we spoke about kids last week, Moe. What about that? Would I be allowed to touch them? Little Bobby fell down and I can't pick him back up or else the big bad wolf will pull me away again."

Moe sat down on the floor next to me and shook his head in disapproval, as if this lady didn't get it.

"I think it's time for you to leave, Anna. There's no reason to bring up that conversation now, because we agreed not to speak about it again."

The door opened suddenly, and Anna stood with the strap of her dress hanging off her shoulder and mascara dripping down her cheeks. She gracefully made her way to the bookshelf and picked up a hardcover. Her face changed and she threw it at me. It didn't hurt—I didn't mind at all to be honest. It was the look on Moe's face that hurt me. His eyes lost their confidence, and he wavered between catching the books and dodging them as she continued to throw volume after volume. Moe ran past the books and caught Anna in his arms.

She struggled and shouted, "Get off me, you prick! You sonofabitch! Heartless prick, get off me!"

She sobbed and gave up, and they leaned against the wall for some time. Moe's face was buried in her hair as tears continuously wet each strand.

Moe unburied his face and made eye contact with me in the mirror hanging on the wall.

"I don't want kids, Anna. I love you, and I'm sorry."

Anna looked at Moe in a loving way and smiled as salty tears entered the creases of her cheeks.

"Goodbye, Moe," Anna said as she took his face into the palm of her hand.

She got up, licked her fingers to wipe away her mascara,

and walked out, closing the door behind her, quiet.

I was alone with Moe now. He walked over to his bar and poured himself a glass of whiskey. His loft was very big, and in each corner there was a different function for the room. Over by the wall-length windows there was a bed on the floor, very low to the ground. A white and blue oriental carpet stopped right before the bed, lying directly in the middle of the loft, and a crystal chandelier hung directly above it.

The kitchen was on the wall across from the bed and had a long wooden table a few feet off the wall that held a bowl of lemons. Pots hung above the table and reflected the crystals onto the wall where the door was.

Under me lay a white floor drop cloth with paint all over it, covering the other half of the loft. There was one station for paints and brushes and another for wood and canvases. To the right of me there was a door that led to the bathroom, and next to it the bookshelf.

I watched Moe, my father, my artist, my creator, drink until he fell asleep above his covers. When he awoke he took a shower and left the loft. He stumbled in around 3 a.m. with a woman with long red hair. It was dark, but I heard their clothing drop to the floor and the sound of their bodies hitting the mattress.

In the morning, the woman made some coffee and walked over to me. She sipped and turned around to see if Moe was looking. She ripped a little piece of wrapping off, and I greeted her. She caressed my cold skin and I realized how I missed being touched. I gave her a chill that moved her body, almost spilling the coffee. I liked making her react. She put on her clothes from the night before and left.

Moe unwrapped me when he awoke. He spent most of the day circling me, examining my every vein. I felt a bit insecure—was I good enough? I doubted he would return me at this point in the process, but those eyes gave me no reassur-

...nce.

He walked a few feet away from me and stared, and then put his finger up and squinted. He walked up to me and slid his hand from my top to my bottom, making his way to my sharp edges. He knocked on me, he hugged me, he ran into me. He made himself a sandwich and kept his eyes on me with every bite.

I watched him as well. He brushed his fingers through his hair as he stepped back to see me from a different angle. I saw his body quiver when he felt me. I saw his lips purse when he felt my corners. He liked me and I liked him.

Over the next few months Moe shaped me with his drill, mallet, and chisel. The only thing I was able to see was that the reflection of my right side in the mirror was disappearing. I was slimming down to my Michelangeloen form. Barely anyone visited during those weeks and, if they did, I was covered with a flannel bed sheet.

It was Moe and I, alone in his space, developing my character and personality. With every hit of the chisel, I felt closer to myself. Every chafe of the sandpaper made me more content with my shape. We were dancing to the rhythmic motion of hitting and reacting. Pieces of me hit the white-smocked floor and added dimension to the Pollock-esque carpet. Moe put all of my shaven pieces into a glass box at the end of each day. I watched my completion through the piled consumption of my past. He hit me, I fell. He picked me up and put me in a box, and I felt more perfected.

I stood in the center of the room, half-made and insecure. Through the thin fabric I could barely make out two figures pressing themselves into each other. I saw my erect penis, bare, white, and cold. It was strange how mine would never be able to do the things Moe's did. Mine would never make a women moan those sounds. Later that night, Moe aggressively ripped off my sheet and sat down on the floor below me.

I looked down at him as he posed, resting his forehead to his knees and wrapping his arms around them with a tight hug.

"Will you continue living when I die?"

He loosened up his grip and laid flat on the flooring, gazing up at me. He sounded weak and jealous, and I didn't like looking down at him like this.

When Moe woke up that morning he went straight back to work, chisel in hand, sculpting me down with rushed hits and loud crashes. It was messy and angry, but my butt was finished and that seemed to be important.

Over the next few days, it became routine where Moe would fuck and then come sit down next to me and speak about leaving a legacy when he died. How I would live out his name, in a way no son ever could.

"When I die, I will live on through you. You are me, and I am you."

I would watch from above as he fell asleep peacefully, knowing that I was awake and always would be awake.

My body was finished, and Moe began working on my face. He worked with a mirror and copied. Our noses were nearly the same, although mine had no bump. His top lip formed more of a heart shape, whereas mine was linear. His eyes were smaller and wrinklier from not sleeping. Mine were lifeless and smooth. I was able to look at Moe now with eyes that he looked at me. My form was a son to Moe.

And I thought, hey, that's great.

A tall older woman with long black hair and red lipstick exhaled as she threw her hand to her heart and gasped. "It's everything. It's nothing. How much?"

Moe poured a glass of water for himself and called her his agent. She spoke of herself in the third person.

"Catherine thinks this is stunning!" She grabbed my behind and put her body against mine. I felt invaded.

76

Moe just stood there, watching.

"It has a bigger penis than you," Catherine said as she reached for my penis. I sent a chill down her spine, and she shivered.

Moe blushed. "I was twenty," he said.

"And Catherine was forty, so what? You're here now, right? Anyway, Moe, baby, I want to get this out. There's hype, the people want more. It's here, you're here. It's ready. Red wine, cheese, some confetti; give me a date, give me a name."

"Two weeks. Francine."

Catherine's perfume lingered in the air for the next few days. The thin sheet was over me while they were setting up for my opening party. Every few minutes I'd see a few men walk by carrying something heavy like a table or a bar. Soon after red, magenta, and yellow lights shined through the sheet on each sixth beat. The lights would start from the entrance and move across the room, landing on me. Red, to magenta, to yellow over and over again. Very loud music began to play. It was the type of music I wanted to throw my hands up to and move my hips back and forth. I couldn't. The beats began to go hand in hand with the lights, and I felt entrapped by this new and exotic world.

"Turn that shit down!" I heard Catherine shout. "It's enough that it'll be playing all night. Who picks this, Moe? What happened to Nina Simone? Or Queen?"

The music changed and the lights slowed down to follow it, and I knew Moe must have been affected by Catherine and her piercing voice. My sheet was aqua blue now, teal circles passing by as if I was underwater.

Suddenly Moe ripped the sheet off of me and grabbed onto my shoulders. I felt safe, and I wanted to touch him back. He looked me in the eyes with his strong stare, and soon his grasp on my shoulders loosened and he stepped back. His eyes traveled down me, examining my veined marble body. He put his hand gently on my cheek and his forehead against my forehead. He closed his eyes. I needed that right then and there. That was when I needed my creator to make sure I was ready for the real world, take my hand, kiss it, and let me go.

An hour into the party I was beginning to understand what these people liked projecting onto me.

"It's almost like his entire being is staring at me and knows all of my secrets. What do you know, Francine? Do you know that I have the sorcerer's stone in my pocket?" a young looking brunette said to me. She brought her index finger to her lips and mouthed, "Shh..."

"I bet Francine knows who shot Biggie," a petite man with round glasses responded.

I shifted my focus to a group of young kids facing my butt. They were all looking at their professor for some kind of explanation or approval of me.

"Students, you're looking at an attempt to rebirth the marble craft. To essentially take on the perfected art and depict it in our current day and age. Can you appreciate the smooth realism of the curves and outlines of the body? Is this too foreign from the Internet age to understand or is there a universal, timeless beauty to this piece of work we have in front of us?"

"We are supposed to feel challenged by this life-size human being. We will die; Francine will remain here in this very position, eyes staring out at the same horizon. Do you take on a Goliath, big macho stance and challenge Francine? Or do you feel in awe of its beauty and infiniteness? Does Francine make you feel temporary? These are the themes I want to read about in your papers. I want you to ask yourself: Is the rebirth working for you? Is it outdated? What do you think the artist intended? Is his attempt working?"

The students stared with blank faces and open mouths at my penis now.

Moe came over to me with a very sophisticated well-dressed woman in all black. She stood up straight and poised herself like a ballerina. When she spoke she fixed her eyes on the listener and followed their pupils anywhere and everywhere.

"It's here, but it's not here. It's real, it's not real." She preached dramatically with her arms moving in wavy circular motions. "It's a cry for help, isn't it? Aren't you?"

She looked me in the eyes now.

"Francine's pseudo-realism is a wake-up call. Where are we now? How far have we come? How much did we grow apart from the Classics? It's a 'fuck you' to new media art. Mr. Williamson, I have a client that would be interested in buying this, is it for sale?"

"Call me Moe. And yeah, talk to Catherine," he said, pointing to the lady in red.

The lights pulsated and the music suddenly seemed louder. Was I ready to go out into the world without my father? How would people understand me without him?

Catherine gave a firm handshake, and the next thing I knew I had a giant red ribbon choking my torso. The gift that didn't want to be given, I repeatedly thought to myself.

***

The marble lobby wasn't as fine as me. It was pure white and led all the way from the foyer up the stairs to the second floor. I was at the foot of the staircase and had the first look at anyone who came through the front. It was fall, so every time someone walked through the brass doors of the townhouse, leaves of all different colors flew in to get some warmth in the midst of the changing temperatures. Cal, the butler who wore a full suit to work every day and was pushing seventy, would escort the visitor in and then sneak over to the front closet to get out the sterling silver broom, sweeping all the leaves back outside. There wasn't much light in the foyer besides the sunlight protruding from the windows in the living room and the antique chandelier hanging a few feet from me. For some reason I always felt as if I was in the dark.

The Hughes family consisted of four immediate family members and a grandfather. Marlene Hughes was ten, the youngest of the bunch. She had black hair cut like a French movie star, short, mid-neck-length hair with bangs. She rarely spoke and preferred sitting with a Sherlock Holmes book when the family gathered every Sunday morning for brunch. Julian Hughes was a little sour in the beginning. He was sixteen and took advantage of his family's affluence. I chose to believe he would grow out of it, which he did eventually, but his family largely gave up on him after he acted out one too many times.

His grandfather, Pat Feinstein, was a famous author with prestigious novels under his belt. He retired to live with his daughter and her family once his wife passed. Pat had a great relationship with Julian because they shared an interest in writing. In my opinion, that bond pulled him out of becoming a dead teen that had crashed his father's Maserati driving home drunk from a party.

Mr. and Mrs. Hughes usually kept to themselves. They both had the same routine every morning, consisting of having the first cup of coffee in bed, the second at breakfast with the family while reading *The New York Times*, and the third in a to-go cup on their way out to work. They returned late at night, usually with business acquaintances they shared. They were good parents so far as a working couple could be. Between them, Pat, and Cal, the kids grew up with dependable parental figures.

At the time I was purchased into the family, I gave my goodbye to Moe. I looked at him for the last time and felt as though I was slowly disappearing and ceasing to exist. I arrived soon after to the townhouse and was greeted with mixed feelings. Grandpa Pat couldn't get enough of me. Marlene touched me and walked away, unimpressed. And Julian was fixated on my penis size. Later, on that first night, he came downstairs in his pajamas while the entire house was sleeping to compare sizes. He walked up the stairs in a heavy manner, and the next day he didn't look at me.

I was adjusting to life beyond Moe because I didn't seem to have a choice. But it was not as scary as I thought it would be. I had a family now that I could watch develop in front of my eyes. The roles had reversed. I moved onto a new part of my form: The parent.

Time passed, and I watched Mr. and Mrs. Hughes go gray. They slowed down their coffee consumption and began coming home earlier from work. Marlene started dating. If she brought the boy inside to the dark foyer, I knew she liked him. She would sit on the loveseat by the staircase and kiss them on the lips once. It began to be a test for her, to see how the boy would react. James, the boy she ended up marrying, was the first boy to stand up after the kiss and leave the rest for the second date.

It was during these nights I got to know the eyes reading all of those mystery stories. She, like her books, lived in secret, in the shadows. Her personhood developed in the dark, outside of the home. Not with anything to hide. Rather, she didn't need the approval of the daytime. Dark soul, I thought sometimes. But she came out a true lady.

On her wedding day, the photographer made us pose together. I still saw the little French haircut running past me and almost tipping me over. I felt scared for her to go, but I knew she had to. I didn't have a choice in the matter.

Julian began publishing short stories and eventually got commissioned by a big publishing house to write his first nov-

81

el. Grandpa Pat passed that year and Julian moved out to focus on his new endeavors. I didn't see much of him after that.

Every now and then I would watch Mr. Hughes on the phone with Julian, walking back and forth past me, tense with nervous energy. I could tell he wanted to state his opinions more often than he did. I think these calls home hurt him... they threatened his current identity. I was comforted by our similarity, dealing with our integrity beyond the shelter of our fathers.

The front door stopped opening as often. I used to think it was because Cal stopped being able to walk fast enough to open it. When there was a visitor, the seasons would bring in their flourishings, whether snow or colorful foliage.

The Hughes retired a few years later and moved into their summer home. Cal didn't go with them. That year the chandelier was never on, and the crystals reflected prisms on the walls. No one came by the house unless it was a messenger retrieving a package to deliver to the summer home. I got used to the walls I was a part of and the room that I belonged to. I was an object just like the stairs, a fixture like the dining room table. I wasn't getting old with the Hughes, I was staying right here. I knew time was passing from the shadows the trees would bring in through the window.

I thought about Moe sometimes, and what he was doing at that moment.

I wondered if he decided to make a baby with Anna, or if he still believed in me being infinite.

BLEEDING RABBIT

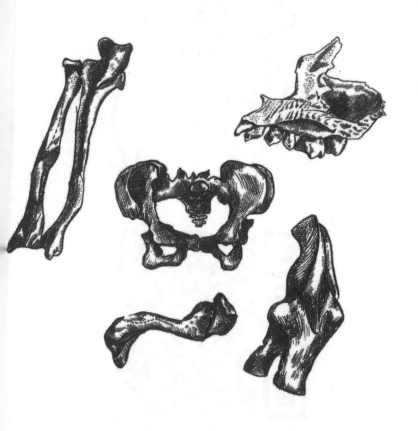

CASSIDY McLOUGHLIN

BLEEDING RABBIT

"The devil's out there beating his wife again," Momma says to Daisy.

Pausing, Myrine collects the plates off the dining table to glance over at Daisy at the windowsill, lost in one of those dreamy stares that only occur in childhood. Outside it's raining, and the sun is still steadily pouring down light. The greens are all stretching out with extraordinary life. Everything's wet and glistening.

Daisy giggles, as she does every time her momma gets to say that.

"Now come along, Daisy. Help me clear off the saucers."

Outside, a rabbit pushes its nose out from under a wide drooping leaf of a bee balm to check how hard the rain's falling. A second later it clumbles out and zips off, fast across the dirt drive and then the whole way across their clearing of a yard. It stops before the tree line on the other side, raises itself up on its hind legs, and surveys all around, its ears flat back.

Daisy's eyes jump. She loves rabbits.

"Look, Momma, a rabbit in the rain," she says. Momma is walking off toward the kitchen, the white clay plates rattling against each other and the thin old silverware stacked on top. There's the constant tinging of the rain against the tin roof too. The sound covers them all like a blanket. The rabbit lowers himself and saunters promptly a few feet over to chew on a bush of honey leaf.

"Daisy Mae, you bring in them other dishes now and help

me wash up."

"Yes, Momma" she says. "There's a rabbit in the rain."

"What's that, Daisy?"

***

David forgets to breathe again. His left hand slides too far forward too quick and he knocks all of the tobacco out of the paper clutched gingerly in his other fingers. It falls all over the tabletop and lands alongside the scraps from a few previous attempts. His face turns red, and he exhales in a long, annoyed sigh. His hands are shaking, and now he's light-headed too. He lowers the paper and plows all the tobacco on the table into a pile and tries again.

Duke is stretched out behind him on the couch underneath the window. He's wearing his fresh pair of dark blue cotton pants because the last ones got wet on the walk back from the mill. The radio stands an arm's length from Duke's head, and the announcer is talking, listing off the names of the gospel tunes they've just heard. It fuzzes warmly in the spaces between his words. Duke hears a loud grunt somewhere in the middle of all of this. He peeps open one of his eyes. David is sitting on the ground near his feet, hunched over the low table. His face is getting near as red as the blood of a cherry pie. Duke starts laughing deeply.

"C'mon, son, you're twelve now. You coulda done this a year ago. Just breathe and sit straight."

David straightens up.

"I'm trying, Pop, I'm just rotten."

And now folks, here in our very own Studio in the Country, we've got the one and only T.J. Rodgers with us and he's gonna sing "Do Lord, Remember Me" to start us off this evening.

Duke closes his eyes again and lays his head back to rest. "You'll get it, kid. Just keep at it."

David licks his upper lip before unconsciously biting his tongue. He holds it, concentrating.

Ting ting…ting ting. The soft tapping of the rain lays over them, again and again. Duke starts to softly sing along the words to the song, his eyes closed and his body tired.

Do Lord, do Lord, do remember me.

The rough-shaven skin of his chin folds and creases dryly with each word.

David, looking up, thinks of how familiar the image feels. The sun and the shade and his father singing.

When I'm on my knees a-prayin'
Do remember me.
When I'm on my dyin' days
Do remember me.

***

The rabbit is under an oak now, away from the wet, and bathing itself. It didn't take Daisy too long to relocate him in the yard. It looks up from its fur and its ears flutter up. Then it turns and scampers away straight into the woods. Daisy scowls and starts to turn away but sees a flash in the distance. She pauses and sees metal black moving through the openings between the trees.

Slowly rumbling on down their drive comes a polished black car, pushing steadily forward toward the house.

"Momma, someone's coming!" she shouts.

"Who's it, Daisy?"

"Can't tell—they're in a car. The rabbit's gone now."

Myrine walks up behind her and puts her hand on Daisy's shoulder, looking to see who's arrived.

***

David lowers his head down and licks the length of the paper, pushes it up and rolls it with his thumbs against his other fingers to try and make it tighter. Done. He holds it close to his eyes to examine. The paper's all crinkled and it's really skinny on one end, fat in the middle, and loose and wide on the other end. It seems a little crooked too, but it's rolled. *How in the world do they do the ones that come in packs?* David thinks to himself.

"Duke, there's a man pulling up in a car!" Myrine shouts from the front of the house.

Duke gets up in silence and walks out.

***

"Well, how are you doing this odd day, Duke?" a tall slick-suited man asks, the door to his sparkling black Nash Ambassador slamming shut behind him. He stands by his car and slides his hands into his pockets, all the while giving the family up on the porch a strange half-faced smirk that only somebody who spent too much time in the city would find appropriate.

"Rested," Duke says, leaning against one of the pillars on the porch next to Myrine and Daisy. "What business has got you coming over to this side of the river?"

The man walks up the steps, removing his hat as he comes under the roof. It's still drizzling, but his black pinstriped suit is fine and dry. Once he reaches the top he nods to Myrine and Daisy.

"Good evening, Ms. Myrine." He looks down to Daisy,

aying, "And aren't you just cute as a bug's ear." He grins at
er before looking back up at Myrine, his bright white and
early-sharp teeth poking out from under his lips. They smile
olitely back at him.

"This is Clyde Boudreaux, Mr. Harvey's eldest," Duke
ays. "Now what business you got over here, Clyde?" Duke
sks with a stern face.

"I think that's something best to be discussed inside."

His jolty crystal blue eyes are a harsh contrast against
)uke's mellowed brown ones. Clyde's eyes hop back be-
ween Myrine, Duke, and even Daisy, not choosing to linger
ong on any of their faces. In response, Duke stares straight
t Clyde, hardly seeming to blink. Nonetheless, he shifts his
ocus to the door and motions toward it.

"If you came all this way then I s'pose it should. Come on
n," Duke says as he opens and holds the door for them be-
ore he follows them in. The heavy spring of the screen door
reaks as it shuts behind him.

"You want some tea? Or a drink?" Myrine asks Clyde.

"A hard drink would be swell. Thank you."

"Well, the whiskey's in the parlor. Let's just go get right
lown to it," Duke says from behind him.

David looks up as they enter. Scraps of tobacco and badly
olled cigarettes ripped or torn in half are scattered all across
he table. He's got two keepers set nicely to the side, apart
from all the chaos.

"Clean that all up and go play outside for a bit."

"Ok, Pop," David says, picking out the pieces of paper and
ossing them into the bin.

Duke walks over to the bar on the other side of the room,
grabs the bottle of Johnnie Walker along with two glasses,
and pours a single into each. David finishes sweeping the leftover tobacco into a giant handful and tosses it back into the
shiny Sir Walter Raleigh tin. He grabs his two keeper cig-

arettes and heads toward the parlor door. Duke walks back over and hands Clyde a glass. He sits on the chair and directs Clyde to take a seat on the couch adjacent. He does.

"Close the door on the way out," Duke says to David right before he's through the doorway. As it clicks he looks straight at Clyde and leans back on the couch. "So you've come all the way out to my house, what can I do for you?"

"The money, Duke."

"Your father and I have a deal about the money."

"Well now my father's dead." Clyde replies, his buzzing eyes moving more than any other part of his body.

***

David, at a slightly frenzied pace, grabs the rough leather pouch out from under his bed, the spare matchbox from the second shelf in the kitchen, and three old cans from under the sink before darting out the door. The rain has all about stopped by now. He walks a short distance out into the woods, knowing exactly the spot he wants to smoke his first hand-made cigarette.

Daisy sees her brother go off and starts to sneak along after him.

"Daisy Mae, you get back here and help me until we finish with these chores! It's not my fault you don't wake up and do yours early like your brother does."

"Yes'm," Daisy says, not fully defeated yet. She keeps her eyes wandering out the windows, scouring the bushes.

***

Somewhere off in the distance David reaches his spot. It's a giant stone sticking out from the foot of one of the first big hills around the house. It's just two small twists away from being in sight of the windows, but it's far enough. It's also hidden from the driveway by a large cropping of live oak. The flat top of the red-gray stone is a little damp, but it'll do. He's found his peace.

He plops on top of the stone, tosses his leather pouch to one side, sets the cans on the other, and pulls one of his keeper cigarettes from his shirt pocket. A little bit of the tobacco has fallen out but that's all right. He puts the skinnier, tighter end in his mouth, then yanks it out again and spits out a few loose chunks of tobacco. He puts it back in, lights the match, and sparks her.

***

"I'm sorry for your loss," Duke says earnestly, unsure of what Clyde wants to come out of the situation.

Mr. Harvey Boudreaux had never really been a friend but not quite an enemy either. Just an acquaintance from the smuggling days who had carried on with more questionable dealings than Duke was generally comfortable with. Not that they hadn't worked together a handful of times when things got bad. When the economy broke, Duke even did some collection work for the old man, hustling down some people he was fairly certain never owed nobody anything, much less Boudreaux. He didn't like it much, although through their shared time there was always a mutual respect between the two of them.

Ever since Clyde had been trying to get along and rise up in his father's business, he'd been making mistakes. Too young to have known the era and game of the rum-running before it was over, he tried to overcompensate with flamboyancy in each of his current endeavors. In short, he was headstrong, and that was a bad thing 'cause he wasn't too bright to begin with.

Clyde shrugs. "I've come to cope. Now I just gotta run everything by myself. And that ain't so bad. A lot fewer obstacles to deal with, I find."

As he shifts on the couch, one side of his unbuttoned jacket falls open enough to reveal a lightly tanned holster strapped around him and hung high on his side. Right on his left ribs. Clyde barely looks down, his eyes quick to dart back up again.

"A lot fewer." He slides his lips apart and smirks right at Duke.

Duke starts to narrow his eyes, then thinks the better of it. Even though his mind is screaming to grab this hotshot-wannabe gangster by the scruff of the neck and toss him right the hell out of his house, he doesn't say a thing of it. He takes a drink, sets his glass down and waits for Clyde to do likewise, then fills them both again. He raises his for a salute.

"To a good friend."

"Naw, none of that," Clyde says bluntly and quickly. He takes a sip, flashing his eyes to the glass and the whiskey disappearing. "I just want the money, Duke. No nostalgia."

"Your father and I had a deal."

"And now my daddy's dead. Deal's off."

***

David spits another few chunks of wet and smoky tobacco out, but he's still enjoying his cigarette. When he exhales he tries to think of the ways he's seen his pop and momma exhaling. They do it so casually. As if the smoke's just walking out the end of the cigarette then falling from the sides of their mouths. But when he tries to inhale it, it just goes straight down into his chest and hurts. He likes the look of it when he blows it out, though. His own personal cloud. He hadn't thought about that part before. For now, he decides to just stick it in one side of his mouth and bite down on it so it doesn't move. That may be how everyone does it.

He slides off the rock and grabs the three empty cans, then walks about twenty paces forward to an old stump and sets them up. Two on the bottom and one on top to make a triangle. Back at the rock he unclasps the brass button on his leather sack and pulls out the smooth wooden slingshot he got for his birthday last year. It always feels good to have it in his hand after a boring rainy day of being stuck inside, cleaning. He turns the open sack upside down. Several handfuls of nicely weighted rocks tumble out.

He shoves a fistful in his pocket for quick reloading, then turns to the cans, places a hefty rock in the leather pad of the slingshot, and pulls back. He holds his breath while he aims at the top can and forgets about the cigarette in his mouth. The smoke flutters up the side of his face and goes straight into his eye.

He spits it out as his eye starts to water and mutters to himself.

"Rotten...stinkin'...nonsense...thing..."

He rubs his eye until it gets right. When it does, he draws back again and aims at the cans.

A rabbit pops out from underneath the big-eared leaf of a Woodbine just a few yards to the side of the cans. David sees it and debates with himself for a second before readjusting his aim. He watches it take a few hops, then sit up on its hind legs, sniffing the air curiously. David pulls back farther on the leather pad and strains the rubber tubes until they almost creak before he lets loose. The rabbit falls down immediately, but its legs kick out sporadically to try and right itself. David, caught up in the surprise of actually having hit it, pauses and then dashes over. Where its eye had been protrudes a mashed-up mixture of flesh covered in rivulets of blood. The rabbit's legs strike out in vain. David stares.

"I'm sorry there, buddy," he says quietly.

Duke stares right at Clyde's crystal blue eyes, staying still and explaining things slowly.

"Well, it's your first time here, kiddo. I haven't even shown you around hardly. Where are my manners? It's a small house so there's not too much here. We've never had too much money, Myrine and I. When I was young I had my share of vice and trouble. That's how I eventually got running in the same circles as your old man. Once times got bad, we didn't have anything backed up. And until I got going down at the mill, we had a little less than nothing. We made by with a quality life, though. Good family, good stories. And we still do. Lemme see…here. You see that photograph right by you? Take a look at that."

Clyde's eyes dash down to the photo for a second.

"That was me right after the war. Had a lot of real interesting stories and times there. I won't—"

"I don't wanna hear about your war—" Clyde tries to interject.

"Well, hold on now. I was just about to say I wasn't gonna bother you with my stories. Actually, I was just gonna explain the decoration."

Duke points straight up. Above the window is an old wooden tomahawk. It has a few chips in the wood of the handle, but the metal and the black of the blade are sharp and clean.

"Now, my grandpaw was lost out in the woods once, in the old days. And he got sprung up all of a sudden by a whole group of Crow. They tried to scalp him with that very same tomahawk."

Clyde's buzzing eyes start to speed up, darting from corner to corner trying to keep occupied. He's only really listening now for the silence.

"And well, my grandpaw solved that little situation. He wasn't a savage, so he didn't scalp them, but he just as well might of. They wouldn't have noticed."

"Damn you, Duke! Just gimme the money so I can get the hell out of here!" Clyde shouts.

There's a pause as Duke waits for the noise to leave.

"I don't have any money. You think anyone has money these days? I know you spend most of your time in the finer parts of the city, but out here in the real country nobody's got nothing to spare. Nothing to give all the folks who come walking around here looking for food or work. Not anymore. As to that small sum your father had lent me, that's been gone for a long time. You'd have to loot every house within twenty miles if you wanted to get that much now."

"Well you better find something—"

As Clyde barks out his words he tries to reach his hand slyly under his coat, but before he can even bring the gun fully level to Duke's chest, Duke is standing on top of his chair, tomahawk in hand, and two of Clyde's fingers, and the gun, are falling to the ground.

WAYNE N.E.

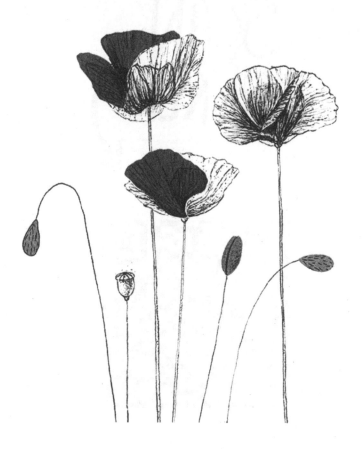

SARAH BIBEL

SCAN HERE!

WAYNE, NE

The oily shadows of Omaha Airport's parking garage clung to the sides of the rental car, their dim tones pulsing between dark and darker each time Mary drove past the concrete columns. Ava watched the light dapple across her mother's face beneath half-closed eyes, the fringe of her eyelashes blurring her view from the passenger's seat. Her neck, cramping and tight, was crooked and bent against the window, but if she moved Ava knew she'd come fully into this scene in the parking garage. She wasn't ready to leave the Benadryl-thick sleep she had been in for five hours on the plane from Massachusetts, so she stayed very still, hardly breathing, keeping her eyes just covered enough to try to trick herself into a half-sleep state where dreams and waking images could be seen at once, a state where the car, her mother, and the drive to her grandparents' nursing home would stay far away from her waking awareness. Ava tried to control her disembodiment this time, to exist somewhat peacefully in the airspace between her lashes and irises, floating just outside of her body.

The flight had been a series of dim sensations, of warmth, soft silence, the occasional ding of the seatbelt sign, and the shuffling of her mother's layered sweaters as she moved in her seat.

There had been one vague dream. A swing set stood in the middle of an empty Nebraskan field. The sky was a big gray cloud, dissolving into the flat horizon. Dead grass in all directions. Ava had been trying to repair the chain that had suspended the seat. The pliers kept slipping. She couldn't do it. Grandma Mona was driven up in a car. She was naked except for a pearl necklace, pearl earrings, white gloves and white dress shoes. Mona walked toward her, arms wide, smiling an open-mouthed smile with a mouth of teeth that shone with collecting saliva.

The undulating light across her mom's face and the echoing sound of the car's tires moving over the grooves of the asphalt caused the space to seem as though it was underwater—where everything was a duller version of what it would be in the harsh light above. Down the lengths of cars, between their metal hides, into the cracks of all the windshields that were left unfixed, the muffled thudding of their borrowed car billowed like disrupted silt along the bottom of a riverbed.

Ava steadily grew more aware of her limbs and organs as the allergy medicine broke down in her veins, absorbed and filtered through her liver. She tried blurring her vision in an attempt to keep kindling the half-dream state and to stay away from the reality of her body. Ava made her mom's features fade and blend into the interior of the car, allowing the arched edges of the window frame to liquefy into Mary's eye socket. The diagonal black streak of the seat belt cut into her neck and fused into a new organ made of flesh and synthetic thread.

She couldn't stay there, though. Her stomach pressed into her, tore her concentration with its loud and nauseous thoughts. Once Ava began to think about her body in terms of separate parts—a sour stomach and a tongue so big that she could choke and gag on it—she had trouble stopping. She was rushing back into her body as if sucked in by a sharp inhale. Mary, beside her, came clearly into focus, while Ava felt as if she was losing sense of her own boundaries.

Ava's forearms pricked with sweat, heat spreading across her face and down her neck. From the pocket of her jacket she

ulled an already halved piece of Trident Original, the skin on
er fingers sticking to the leather pocket.

"Are you chewing that because you want to, or because
ou feel sick?" Mary asked.

"Sick."

Ava's breaths felt like nothing, as if air was being stolen
rom her and she couldn't get it back. Each exhale was a ghost.

"Too much gum is bad for your teeth."

"It helps."

"How?"

"It's worse to sit still and think about it." Breathing was
ike mouth to mouth without exhaling. Hot. Stale. "I feel sick.
'm not just saying it."

"Sure, I know."

When Ava began to feel this way, her mom always reminded her that states like this never lasted and would invariably
pass. Ava wasn't her anxiety. *I am not my nervous stomach, I
am not my dizziness. I am more than my elevated pulse.*

Mary drove, unblinking toward the exit. Light from outside the garage began to color the tip of her nose and the
rounded swell of her cheeks. At the traffic gate, she reached
over and squeezed Ava's shoulder. Her brief touch brought
the burning sensation of crying to Ava's throat, although her
eyes remained dry. The hand, her mother's hand, became a fo-
cal point of warmth against the edge of her shoulder. She tried
to ground herself around that point of contact, to sit solidly
in the seat next to her mom, where the anticipation of frozen
fields and Mona and Joe alone in a room could exist inside her
mind without distress. *There is a difference between pain and
discomfort*, her mom often said.

"Sit up, you'll feel better. Put your window down for a few
minutes. Breathe."

The shadows dissolved around the car as Mary pushed forward into the swelling light of the access road.

***

When trying to picture Mona, Ava's mind quickly confused itself, and instead of her grandmother, Mary's face began to solidify behind Ava's eyes. It had been five years since Ava last saw Mona, and there were details of that face she couldn't remember. Her mother's features seeped in. Mary's face with Mona's gray curls. Mary's hazel eyes with Mona's rounded glasses, her eyes distorted by the glass's glare—the image shuddering with the backdrop of some nowhere field, dead grass in all directions. A broken swing, a big gray cloud.

As if there was still the darkness of the garage trapped in Ava's hair, dimness curled around her ear and inched its way into her head, like a worm, trying to stay inside her. Her mom usually knew how to make her feel better—less anxious, less like a ghost outside of her body looking in—but not this time. Ava rubbed her hands against her ears, shook out her hair, and pressed the button to make the window go down. She put her face half outside the car and tried to take deep, even breaths. She tried to focus on watching the concrete and curved glass of the airport fall behind in the rear-view mirror. Soon, ranch style houses and empty sidewalks replaced the asphalt columns. The world flattened around them.

"Well, we won't be there by noon. Joe will just have to stay until we get there. There's usually no traffic outside the city, though," Mary said. "Do you feel any better?"

Ava knew that Mary knew she wasn't feeling better—maybe better than before, but not completely better. Maybe she never would. When someone felt worse than normal for long enough, it was easy to lose track of what it was like to feel normal again. There was no direct path back to homeostasis. Previous feelings folded in on themselves and disappeared, so that the phrase "You feeling any better?" eventually lost all

meaning because there was no betterment, no point of refer-
ence; just different sensations from moment to moment.

Ava let one arm unfold out the window, gravity hyperex-
ending her elbow, making her reach for the dead grass. The
pale underside of her forearm, with blue veins swimming beneath, was turned up toward the blank sky. Her head was fully
engulfed by rushing winter wind, but she still couldn't find
her breath.

Thoughts, like a hot edge, cut thro—

Ava's mind was like a hot metal edge. Thoughts never cut
all the way through, never completed the cycle of images that
entered and exited. They got stuck somewhere in the middle of her brain, seizure twitching around the soft pink ma-
terial, twitching through the parts of her that controlled scent
and sex drive and memory. She closed her eyes and she was
stuck in some rancid montage on loop. Thoughts cropped
up like grass after a heavy rain—nothing and then suddenly
it was everywhere, spreading over trees, rocks, anthills and
rabbit holes. Without warning in social studies, eating dinner
at home, reading a book, and those images, someone else's
images, came frothing behind her eyes, overgrown in an in-
stant. The scenes glitched. People talking made one sound
over and over again, their faces moving forward and reset-
ting, stuck. The sound of the scenes were turned up and sharp.
The lights were too bright and saturated and pricked like pins.
They stung. Sometimes, her dreams spilled into her waking
thoughts while she was open-eyed in bed, trying to quiet the
ongoing reel of images—the inside of her head, burning from
the speed of it all.

***

Sixty-two miles down the country highway, Mona and her
husband, Joe, waited in Wayne.

Wayne, a town with a public pool and a high dive, a park where the ice cream truck would come right before sunset, sudden summer storms with warm rain, steaming pavements, the static of cicadas and the whisper of tall grass cast in moonlight.

Wayne, with its wild rabbits and circling hawks.

Wayne, with eleven summers of Ava's life written into its history—if towns kept histories.

Her footsteps and fingerprints were all over the town. She had a habit of picking at her cuticles. She couldn't stop herself; there was satisfaction in the idea that she was leaving a little bit of herself behind everywhere she went.

Her skin, scattered all across Wayne.

***

Ava came home from school after dark. The walk had been cold, windy with dead leaves hitting her ankles, which were exposed below the edge of her jeans. Her eyes burned with the after image of college applications with repetitive questions: Mother's name, Father's name, their highest earned degree, your intended major, your second choice, what does a liberal arts degree mean to you? Will you treat your education like a privilege? Why are you worth the space here, *why are you worth any space?*

The house was dark except for one illuminated room deep inside. She threw her weight against the front door, thick wood always jamming. The vibration of glass echoed across the porch. Again, Ava thrust her shoulder into the carved wood, wanting to be surrounded by four walls and out of the vastness of the February night. Metal scratched against metal, the house groaned against her, and the door fell forward. The opening became a vacuum as the murk of winter with its crescent moon, damp moss smells, and the orbs of street lights

106

reatened to fall into the quiet and warmth of the mudroom.

Ava felt as if she was sinking closer to the earth with each tep. Her mom sat hunched over a laptop, small amongst her tacks of papers, succulents crowding in on all sides, over-owing in their misshaped ceramic bowls. The bloated plants lowed in the light of the laptop.

**

They rounded the exit ramp toward NE-15, and Mary tried o find the dial to turn the heat on. She pressed buttons at ran-lom, glancing between the dashboard and the sloping road. horned bushes, overgrown, prickled around the car and the oad. Ava could almost reach them. She imagined stretching ut to grab fistfuls of spurred branches, squeezing them in her ands until blood collected along her lifeline and her love line nd the wrinkle of her palm that said how many children she vould have.

Ava pulled her hand inside the car, put the window up, her ight arm now cold against her body. How many children she vould have? She looked at her hand, scratching a fingernail long a purple line in her palm. Wind whistled through the alf-cracked window. Ava pulled the button, sealing the in-ide of the car from weeds, chucks of dirty snow, and empty ows of crops. Parenthood seemed more morbid the older Ava grew. It felt evil, she thought; it was evil to create something hat had to watch you die.

As she pulled off the exit, Mary cut off the only other car on he approaching highway, still searching for heat. The man— face red, mouth open and twisting—punched the ceiling of nis gray Sedan and swerved around them, speeding toward he horizon. Harder than she meant to, Ava pushed her mom's hand away from the controls. Mary's knuckles hit the steering wheel, the slap of bone against hard plastic loud in the silence of the car. Mary's breath hissed through her teeth.

"Mom, let me do it," Ava said, pressing the correct but
ton and turning the dial up. Mary massaged her hand before
pressing the knuckles into her thigh. The symbolic wavy lines
on the dashboard lit up orange.

"I hardly touched you," Ava said, watching Mary frown
her mouth downturned. "Wait, did I actually hurt you?"

"The cold makes my hands ache. It should be fine in a sec
ond." Mary pressed again and again into the soft fabric of her
navy sweatpants. Her knuckles looked white and enlarged
her skin pulled tight across them.

"I have arthritis in a few places, you know." She shrugged
smiled. "It happens."

Ava turned away. "I'm sorry," she said, hardly moving her
lips. Advanced inflammatory arthritis could cause the erosion
of joints. She focused on a red farmhouse in the distance,
stark against the dim fields. Lengths of decaying wooden
fences blurred past them—and then, as if the passing world
was a roll of double exposed film, she saw an advanced stage
of arthritis. The acute swelling of her mother's joints led to
crystallizing bone spurs; large masses grew underneath the
skin, stretching it too thin, the flesh ripping along the curves
of her knuckles. She saw inflamed skin, the rub of bone on
bone imposed on rotten wood of the collapsing sides of the
house. Ava pressed her fingers into her closed lids. Prairie colors—rust, mustard yellow and green—exploded toward her
from the darkness.

***

"Ava, we have to go see her before she, I don't know—"
Mary's voice weakened, high-pitched in its attempt to keep
going. Her eyes looked lost behind glasses reflecting the
computer's light. "—loses the ability to talk all together." She

raised her hands above the table, above the computer, holding them in suspension, fingers shaking. It made Ava feel as if she was looking at a new person in her dining room, an actress playing her mother. This was the scene where the mother cried to the daughter about her own dying mom. The image would fade to black and reopen on the next morning: sunny, with coffee brewing, toast on the table. But Mary stayed there, lips pressed tight together, pushing all the blood out.

Mary let her hands fall back onto her thighs, hard. "I mean, she couldn't even..." The muscles in her neck strained as she lost control of her voice. "She could hardly say anything other than 'right, right, right' when I called today. I don't even know if she realized it was my voice. She sounded like she—" Mary couldn't finish the sentence. Her face was folding in on itself, turning into the inside of a rose with the petals ripped away, twisted and flushed. Then Ava was at her shoulder, pulling her mother's head toward her chest, hot tears cooling quickly on her wrist. The glasses fell onto Mary's thighs, her hands still where they had landed, bony fists gripping at her sweatpants.

—was disappearing. Ava finished her mom's sentence quietly in her head. *She sounded like she was disappearing.* Her grandmother was alone in her decline. Even with a husband, she was still alone in her own body, left to turn to dust that would blow away in any Midwestern storm. Ava tried to breathe with Mary; she was sinking into the ground beneath the dining room table, moving past the green flowered tablecloth, the dirty napkins, past the mountains of plants, leaves, soil, and past her mother's feet—into the earth below.

***

Dementia: *A general term for a decline in mental health severe enough to interfere with everyday activity. It is not a specific disease. Dementia is often incorrectly referred to as* *'senility' or 'senile dementia', which reflects the formerly widespread but incorrect belief that serious mental decline is a normal part of aging.*

__Vascular Dementia:__ A decline in thinking skills caused by conditions that block or reduce blood flow to the brain. Brain cells are deprived of vital oxygen and nutrients. Cells die after multiple minor strokes, strokes so minor the patient may not even realize this is happening.

Vascular brain changes often coexist with changes linked to other types of dementia, including Alzheimer's disease and dementia with Lewy bodies. Several studies have found that vascular changes and other brain abnormalities may interact in ways that increase the likelihood of dementia diagnosis. Many experts believes that vascular dementia remains underdiagnosed, although it is widely considered the second most common cause of dementia after Alzheimer's disease, accounting for ten percent of cases.

Sign up for our e-news to receive updates about Alzheimer's and dementia care and research.

Ava hadn't known any of this until she googled it late the night before their flight to Nebraska. Mona's brain, without her ever knowing, had been choking. The cells suffocating while she went grocery shopping, and cooked dinner, and laid beside Joe.

Cumulative damage, damage gathered over time. Multiple small strokes or other conditions that affected blood vessels and nerve fibers deep inside the brain—it could cause more gradual thinking changes as damage accumulated. By the time doctors diagnosed it, the cells were already dead.

There were no test for dementia, the website explained. Just a careful monitoring of symptoms. Ava wasn't sure of Mona's symptoms. Common early signs of widespread small vessel disease could include impaired planning and judgment, uncontrolled laughing and crying, declining ability to pay attention, and impaired function in social situations and difficulty finding the right words. Aging did not coincide with serious mental decline. But Mona's aging had.

Dementias were usually progressive. According to the website, it meant if a person or their loved one was experiencing memory loss or any changes in thinking ability, they should see a doctor. Because vascular cognitive impairment often went unrecognized, many experts recommended professional screening with brief tests to assess memory, thinking and reasoning for everyone considered to be at high risk. Ava knew vascular dementia would now always be a part of her family medical history. She couldn't stop herself from thinking back and gathering together all of Mary's increased moments of forgetfulness. She couldn't stop herself from doing some kind of dementia equation where she took out Mona and replaced her with her own mother, dividing their age difference and adding each instance of memory lapse.

Professional screening for depression were also recommended for high-risk groups. Depression commonly coexisted with brain vascular disease and could contribute to cognitive symptoms.

The website burned on her screen; it was the only light on in the house, maybe the entire street. While Ava remained awake, the air was thick with the breaths of an entire neighborhood asleep.

There is no treatment or cure that stops its progression.

Ava paused there for a long time. She couldn't tell how long.

There were medications and treatments that could address symptoms, but patients and their families and close friends were basically on their own—sons and daughters watching their parents forget what groceries they just bought, the name of their friends, how to get home; they would watch them forget when to laugh or cry, how to feed themselves, how to get to the bathroom.

And even when Mona lost the ability to speak to others, she might retain clear internal thinking and thoughts.

Please sign up to our e-news to receive our newsletter for more information and updates on v a s c u l a r d e m e n t i a.

***

Mona and Bill grew up in Lincoln and met during college. They were devoted Huskers, their closets filled with red sweatshirts. But then Bill was offered a good job at a pharmaceutical manufacturer in New Jersey, and Mona found out she was pregnant with Mary, who would be the oldest of their six kids. In Scotch Plains, their house looked as though it had been uprooted by a Midwestern tornado and dropped on the East Coast. Everything was either turquoise, burnt orange, sage green, or tan—colors of the plains. Every other item in their house had a chicken, rooster, or a chick on it. Mona wore her cowboy boots when she did yard work. As soon as their kids were out of the house, they sold the place and moved back to Wayne. Their skin had missed the uninhibited sun and free moving breeze. Mona and Bill were intertwined with the cornfields, the long stretches of empty highways, and the antique shop downtown.

Bill met Ava once, when she was a year old. He died the next year. Mona married Joe a few years later. They met at Chicken Days—Wayne's version of a county fair. He was a chicken and soybean farmer, but that day he was running a pancake breakfast stand. Mona had been wearing one of her favorite rooster sweaters.

Joe owned half a million chickens, collecting around 375,000 eggs a day. After he met Mona, he renamed every chicken after her. *This is Mona No. 147,300, this is Mona No. 537, this is Mona No. 293,520.*

The earth was frozen. Ghosts of Nebraskan crops lay in the barren stretches of field as they moved toward the horizon. *Corn as high as an elephant's eye.* That's what Ava's mom and dad used to say on this same drive when she was younger. But that had been in the summer. Today, crumpled skeletons of corn stalks and husks had been abandoned in their rows. The acres of hay, alfalfa, and soybeans were empty except for scatterings of weeds and a light coating of snow.

They hadn't come to Nebraska every summer, but on and off throughout her childhood Ava had come to Wayne for Chicken Days and the fourth of July. One time, they flew to Seattle, rented a car and drove through Glacier National Park, Yellowstone, and ate huckleberry pie all the way to Wayne. Another time, they drove straight across the country from Massachusetts.

They stopped in towns with only one main road, where the children had to take the bus for hours to get to school each day, towns that Ava's father said would disappear soon. She had asked him what he meant, and he'd replied, "One day there won't be enough people for a town and it'll just stop existing. Towns and cities don't last forever."

He turned down the volume of his *Route 66 Revisited* CD and pointed to a passing sign that read: Modale, Pop. 283. They had been somewhere in Iowa.

"I'm sure there's no school there anymore. I'm sure they need to go to the next town to get groceries. How long do you think people will stick around there? It doesn't have the things they need. They'll move somewhere else. And then, it'll be abandoned, a ghost town."

Up until that moment, Ava hadn't realized she had thought

towns lasted forever. But she must have on a certain level, because her father's words made her feel lonely in a way she had never felt before. She pictured kids, like her, on hot buses and in abandoned diners where dust would collect on the patent leather seats. She pictured people packing up their cars and leaving their childhood homes. Ava began to feel outside of herself, thinking of all the ghost towns that existed that had never crossed her mind, with empty spaces in abandoned rooms that once held families. She turned the volume of her Walkman all the way and wouldn't look outside until they reached the hotel in Lincoln.

Nebraska had always been summer to Ava. It had always been the tail end of tornado season, the time of summer thunderstorms.

Five years ago, Ava had been on the same highway in a different rental car. A purple minivan with the same masked smell of smoke as this one. She had been in sixth grade. Her hair had been long, dyed in streaks of magenta, and she remembered the feeling of contentment that came with feeling no discomfort. It was as if every part of her had worked together in synchronicity. She never had excess thoughts about her stomach or the tightness in her throat. Each working piece of her must have been cohesive then, because she couldn't remember ever feeling the way she did now—with her jeans cutting deep across her belly button, her thoughts circling round and round, and the dull waves of nausea rushing up to her lips.

She tried to find that comfort again, tried to find it in the familiar smell of the unfamiliar car, in the nearly recognizable landscape. As their car moved them past field after field, Ava watched the frost-dusted earth sparkle, and thought it seemed wrong—it was wrong to see this place in the winter.

Each year she grew taller, she grew further outside her skin.

Mary sat tense at the wheel, gripping and releasing her hands. They were late. Joe was waiting for them so he could leave for work. Mona couldn't be left unattended for long. Ava picked at the skin around her fingers. The crescents around her chipping polish were raw. Pinpricks of blood formed around her thumbnail. Mary slapped her own face; the sharp noise made Ava jump.

"Why would you do that?" Ava asked. Her jaw tightened and ached, her teeth locked together.

"I'm trying to stay awake." Mary continued to tap her face, keeping one hand on the wheel as she alternated cheeks.

Ava could see her left leg pulsing in time to the blows. She felt her own legs begin to cramp. Her knees ached against the glove compartment, stuck between the seat and the body of the car. She tried to imagine her grandmother, what she looked like when she smiled, but every time an image began to form the face never fully focused. It stayed blurred—contorted. Her mouth looked as if it was opening too wide.

"Mom, stop," Ava said, wanting to reach out to quiet the tick of Mary's hands, the bones protruding from under the thin skin.

Instead, she cleared her throat. "What's this place like?" A few years ago, Mona and Joe had moved into Three Oaks, the assisted living home that had been built down the block from their house. The last time Ava had seen them, they were living in the home she had come to associate with Wayne— ranch style, at the end of a cul-de-sac. An alfalfa field that was bordered by an empty, grassy lot filled with dandelions in the summer.

"Oh, you know. It's fine. They're still very independent. It's almost like an apartment, but with doctors." Mary's hands kneaded the steering wheel. "She says they like it. They were able to move a lot of their stuff into their suite, which must have been comforting, I guess. A while ago she told me she

115

liked the collection of movies they have. I don't know if she spends much time outside their room. I imagine it's hard. They can see their old house from the windows."

"Yeah, I guess. Hard," Ava said. Strange, she thought, it must be strange and impossible to watch the house they once called home from a new window. A *For Sale* sign on the front yard, groups of strangers gathering on the porch, looking out of windows back at Mona. Mona, alone in what would be her last home, the aid in the next room and Joe at work.

All of Ava's summers ran together, fast like a mountain creek flowing through her memory. Beyond the window of the car, solid slates of gray clouds were thickening across the sky. The barrier between the dusky fields and the spaces above them were dissolving. She saw Mona looking out and seeing strangers mowing her lawn, strangers killing her plants. Ava needed to get out of the car, stretch her legs and walk into those fields. She needed to feel the soil beneath the soles of her shoes and make it feel real. Real like it had been so solidly five years ago.

The first thing anyone saw when approaching Wayne was the water tower at the end of Ava's grandparents' street. It was situated on the one sloping hill in the town, white and ridged up the side, sky blue on its bulging top. WAYNE, AMERICA was painted in tall black letters over the blue. Mona's house stood at the highest point in Wayne. The rest of the town seemed to ease off of their lawn, a gradual decline until the main highway. Wayne was a small mound of dirt in the dried sea of Nebraska plains, the world sanded down around it.

Ava could see it unfold before her—a generational equation. The women in her life taking the bodies of their elders, like hermit crabs who outgrew their shells. Naked and exposed, with nowhere to go except toward a new body.

Ava kept her eyes on the water tower as Mary took the exit toward downtown. The dark sky made the edges of the tower glow and shiver. The longer she stared the faster the sky moved behind it, as if the clouds were rushing past, the tower leaning forward across the town. Mary hit the brakes, jerking Ava forward. Her eyes refocused on a woman trying to lead her child across the street. The mother was waving her hand in front of the girl's lost and distant face, trying to snap her toddler out of her trance. They were the only people on Wayne's Main Street.

Downtown, the three major roads were paved with cobblestones. Their car rolled over the rocks, the tires roaring across the uneven ground. Ava used to jump from stone to stone, using her toes to balance. She was always barefoot there. They passed the two-screen movie theater—Majestic on Main. Five years ago, Ava went to see *Chicken Run* with her dad and they could only sit in certain parts of the theater because rows had been sectioned off with caution tape. The roof was brittle from water damage and had begun to crumble.

They passed the coffee shop where Ava's uncle, Bob, had tried to teach her how to play chess. She'd forgotten immediately, but it was the closest she had ever felt to him. He had been patient, giving her time to make mistakes. He let her try his coffee, even though he knew Mary never let her have any.

And next to the café was the antique shop, the one that would sometimes surge into Ava's mind. Mona amongst the old furs, the rusted metal and frosted glass. In Ava's memory, she was somewhere near ten, she'd just turned her head to look behind her, and there was the repeating image: through strands of her own hair, Mona reaching to touch a teacup, purse strap in one hand, eyebrows coming together, eyes glistening.

Last, they passed Swan Creek, Mona's favorite boutique. The mannequins in the window wore turtlenecks and sweaters with embroidered flowers on the chest. Ava could hear the child cry in the distance behind them, but soon they were far down the road, spiraling up toward the tower.

A mind of cow paths, her mom used to say to her. *You have a mind filled with cow paths*. Anxious thoughts had been spreading like the root systems of prairie grass through her head more rapidly than ever before. Maybe they had begun by accident—one thought led to another led to the feeling of a tight throat, nausea, as if her mind was separating from her body. Her inner voice would feel too loud, a bursting pile of dead grass cracking against her skin, too tight around her. And when it happened it felt as if it could never end. How could it possibly end? Time and time again, the same pattern, the same skeletal cows walking the paths from one thought to the next and back again until the grass was beaten down, worn away to exposed earth and yellowing broken stalks. There were grooves that had formed in her mind, and no matter how self-aware she was, she couldn't stop those cows that were lame with overwork and malnutrition lumbering off the main road, away from logical comforting thoughts, down the cow paths into half-dead fields. Dead ends. Holding cells. Rooms in a slaughterhouse.

Mary turned down Mona's street, and for a moment, they were within the two o'clock shadow of the tower. It was just beginning to snow. Ahead of them, on the left side of the street, was Mona's house. The grass was dead. The plants in the garden that ran alongside the porch were masses of barren twigs. The skeletal systems of the once lush rose bushes, black-eyed susans and coneflowers looked sharp against the muted landscape. New and partially constructed houses were beginning to fill in the empty lots along the street.

Ava squinted to bring the fields at the end of the cul-de-sac into focus. Her stomach felt as though it was filling with acid.

Where the road had always ended in a jagged line of broken concrete a new sheet of asphalt stretched into the distance. Her cul-de-sac was now a continuous road. The alfalfa and cornfields had been reduced to small patches on either side.

When she was younger, she'd tried to run through the fields of corn like she had seen girls do in Western movies, but it had been harder than she thought it would be. The spaces between the stalks were narrow, and the shoots of corn were hard; it had hurt when she slammed her shoulder or hit her hand on them. She hadn't made it very far. Ava ended up walking out, tripping every few feet.

The tower was at one end, the house at the other. A house at the end of the cul-de-sac.

It was as if the world ended and began up there.

She could stand at the edge of the pavement and watch the world drop off around her.

***

The corridor that led away from the reception desk was carpeted a musty blue. It swallowed every sound they made, leaving just the noise of the friction of their clothing, the sound of their breathing. The walls were off-white with dark green trim. It all looked false to Ava. Like how hotels were cleaned constantly to the point where there was no trace of the people who inhabited the rooms. Everything at Three Oaks felt as if it had been placed just so to make guests and inhabitants feel at ease. Most doors had decorations, wreaths or ornaments hanging on them with the names of the people who lived there. Some had flowers or small baskets of candy. Even these signs of personality and hominess seemed calculated.

Ava readjusted her backpack and tried to pull her jeans above the fold of flesh below her belly button. Stepping out of the car hadn't done much to stop the feeling that everything that touched her skin cut in too deep, inciting nauseous breaths. She passed two doors with no decoration, just the room number nailed in the center. Ava pictured emptiness behind the door—a family clearing out the last possessions of their loved one, throwing out the leftover food. The rooms were being reset.

Mona and Joe's room was at the end of the hallway, to the left side. Across the door was a wooden sign with the words *Joe and Mona Welcome You* painted in cursive. There was a small wreath as well, made of yellow and red flowers with miniature chickens and eggs glued in an alternating pattern around it. Next to the door, a rubber mat was laid out with a pair of heavy work boots, weighed down by thick layers of dried dirt.

Before knocking on the door, Mary called out, "Hello, we're here!" in a tone that made Ava's upper lip twitch. Mary was smiling to herself, chuckling awkwardly. Maybe it was nervous laughter. No answer came from inside. Ava could hear the muffled sounds of a television. The words, almost undetected, were stripped of their meaning. The sounds of an almost English language became an alien dialect. Mary knocked again and then turned the knob. It was unlocked.

Ava grabbed her mother's shoulder. "Wait, come on, don't do that, they might be—"

"They might be what? Let's go," Mary said, walking inside.

The familiar smell her grandmother's couch gave off when she would sit and read stories to Ava swallowed her as she stepped into the room. Looking around felt like dream logic—everything was just similar enough to the inside of their old home. It made Ava dizzy to see the unsettling familiarity. No lights were on, but the entire wall they faced was a sliding glass door, letting in the last of the sun's glow. The gray tint of a slow setting sun behind winter clouds was cast upon everything—the orange-tweed sofa, the tall cabinet of Mona's teacup collection, the ceramic roosters. It was a light that made every object look waxen, with tumid shadows gathering beneath tables and in corners.

Mary stepped in front of Ava, the same light washing over her. Her skin turned ashen, a collection of organs and arthritis. Ava's stomach was sinking toward the earth. Mary looked tired, her eyes moving over every object. She seemed to be tallying up the furniture and trinkets, a distant haze in her stare. She let out a slow, deep sigh. To their left was a small kitchen, and across the counter both could see a sliver of the bedroom.

Joe was standing over Mona, who was sitting on the bed, facing him. The TV was on full blast in the background. It cast moving shadows across the two stagnant bodies. Their faces pulsated purple, yellow, blue—there was the sound of children laughing from some sitcom. Joe was cupping Mona's chin with one hand, the other pressed on her thigh. It was hard to tell if he was saying anything or just staring at her. Their faces were close, and Mona was looking at him with intense concentration, her hands at her sides. Ava watched Mary observe them. She wanted to go back outside and knock on the door. She wanted to give them this moment, and let them re-arrange for an actual entrance where Mary and Ava would step through the door to where her grandmother and step-grandfather would stand just inside, smiling and open armed, waiting to hug their long missed relatives. Instead they had broken into this moment too quickly, intruders of some intimate ritual.

"Joe. I'm sorry we're late." Mary's voice sounded wrong, off, like an incorrect note. Mona stayed sitting, her face lowered, still turned away from them.

Joe moved slowly but with the strength of someone who had been active his entire life. He wore a denim button down shirt that was pulled tight across his bulging stomach. The shirt was tucked neatly into thick Levi's; a heavy brown belt with a shining buckle held them up. He had what Mary used to joke was the Nebraska body. Big belly supported by thin strong bowlegs.

"Mary," he said, pulling her into a quick, rough hug. He patted her twice on the back, never letting his touch linger. "It's fine. I'm just going to have to stay later tonight. Need to make sure shipments are out for tomorrow."

"We missed lunch, didn't we?" Ava couldn't see Mary's face, just the back of her head. Her short graying hair was shooting off in different directions, messy from when she had fallen asleep on the plane.

Joe made a noise of affirmation. Mary started to apologize again, but Joe just pressed his hand to her shoulder. He looked over at Ava. She stayed by the door, so he had to make his way over to her. He put his arms around her in the same brisk embrace.

"Ava," he mumbled, hardly opening his lips. Ava smiled and gave him a brief squeeze before he pulled away. He took a stiff jacket from a closet next to Ava, excusing himself for having to say goodbye so quickly, and letting them know how to reach Mona's aid if they needed anything. The door closed with a click, and then the three of them were alone.

Ava couldn't move. She watched her mom walk to the bedroom, bend to hug Mona, slowly rubbing her back for a moment. She kissed the top of her head. For a second, as Mary was straightening up, their faces aligned perfectly, each in profile. They looked so similar. Ava's breath caught in her throat, the sound of her heart filling her ears, loud, numbing. The noises coming from the TV distorted around her, incoherent and strange.

Mary moved her arms to get Ava's attention. She raised her eyebrows and pointed to the ground next to her. Ava dropped her bag in the entrance to the kitchen. She walked around the counter and into the bedroom, trying to breathe out her anxty.

"Hi, Grandma," Ava whispered, her throat thick and lined with mucus. Trying to smile, she wrapped her arms over the top of Mona's shoulders. She was surprised by how much she needed to tighten her grip, by the way Mona seemed to shrink away from her, so much smaller than she had anticipated. Her sweater slowly decompressed, and finally Ava reached bone—the true outline of her grandmother revealing itself through their bodies pressed together. Mona lifted her hands and patted Ava's hips. Three pats. Strong, crisp pats.

"Hi, Grandma. I missed you."

"Right, right. Hello." Moving away from her again, Ava watched a smile twitch across Mona's face. She seemed to be trembling, but she held Ava's gaze. Her eyes were damp, shining, and she kept wringing her hands together on her lap. Mary gripped the top of Ava's shoulder from behind. The pressure was so comforting, Ava had to stop herself from crying out—her chest swelled, filling with warmth.

SELECTED POETRY

DREW ANDERLA

THESE TIMES

You know, these are dream-synth times—
times to be mistrustful of
self-proclaimed authenticity
and its mistress, the first person perspective.

These are times to make
sounds and suggestions
rather than theses and chatter—

Someone asked you, "what's the matter?"
it's a good question, though one
perhaps unanswerable
in an atmosphere filled
with fog from machines to
provoke nostalgia for a time
before anti-smoking regulations.

In the blue stage light
you turned to each
other and decided:
you that he could be enough,
he that you could not.

See,   the hardest thing
is realizing that someone else spotted
insufficiencies you toiled
to keep secret—

Insecurity adorns you like
a Botticellian halo—

it's hard to tell what
people are
and what they're
doing
most   times
but especially
these—
these times
they are
they is
they ain't
no faster than they were,
just   more crowded—

and   in this perception of chaos
you   grab at yr   man's waist
like you
don't
get
the   significance of
a
glance
first ave cab
2 a. m.   down
the tunnel near the U N

the
un
un
undulating
street
lights
un
un

                    un d er
              un
                              un
              un
        you boys unspeaking
                        there
            it go go goes
                    unspoken   and
                    misunderstood
yr chest   hair
          intertwines,   you grab
              his   cock
              once   more the
            cars drive by
                                    un
                    cast
              un
          dul at ing
          lights   up
        at   the
            ceiling.

        we've   expressed   years
          in light shows
                    on ceilings—

SELECTED POETRY

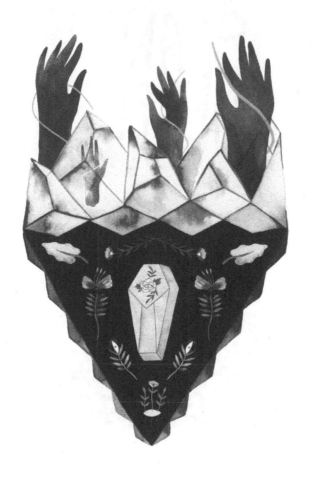

TOM KRANTZ

BURN MARKS

22 with the hair of a 40-year-old,
body of a jelly roll and the swollen
temples of a wrinkled drunk

if the feet aren't brittle
they're burning in water
hands—the pin board
of microscope scars

and a mouth like an impacted
crater or toilet

has anyone told you the poet's stomach
is a suitcase of drugs and slosh, foaming
at the rusty throat in a subway cart
where everybody is trying to feel nothing

where no one smokes or gets headaches
because their drinks always come in
glasses with rims, decent people
who cum in socks and keep the volume low
decent commuters with indecent thoughts
septic minds—sardines on the 7

witness the routine suicide
everyone survives, suits and elastic,
young love and lily peddlers
nobody cares that the flowers
smell like dog piss.

Them bodies like advertisements,

say you can love a job but hate
the schedule, hate the time
the time
the time,
ticking like aluminum cans
in the trash, a more honest vase
a resting place for forgive me bouquets.

everyone wants to feel nothing.
Every unwilling Buddha
with an iPhone leaves their seats
in all the ways a fly wishes to leave the paper.

You take the long way home,
stare at the peddler's reflection
in the lily nectar while somewhere,
in some studio, the publisher counts
all the dollars in your words.

Leah

And the burning foot feels
the way a cough sounds in public.

The death of a friend
is only remembered
when the work shift ends.
Coworkers will remind you of this

when they tell you he passed
while I was wiping down counters.

Co-people take out their impulse
to break down with the trash.

Nobody cries until
the shift drink settles.

***

Work absorbs the physical—
the marrowed pain that aches
in the peripherals.

Should you consider this
a blessing than pray
to the customer.

Another refill to soothe a break up.
We pray in the name of
the father.

A complaint to scatter the ashes of a friend.
We look toward the sky for
the sun.

Neighbors now entangled
in accident steel, take a backseat
to clocking out and we say.

Another holy ghost saved
from the dinner rush.

***

The insensitive,
such as myself
don't mourn
the presence of death
in the same way
we don't hang
our heads for the unborn
(the same lines I used
when we got the abortion).

We just offer a cigarette
and say that's life, and death
love and loss.

I chalk it up to nothing more
than chalkboard specials.

***

Not until I'm underground
do I remember you. Leah,

I try to chisel your memory
out of pebbles on the beach.

Attempt to recreate the village
where we once lived, but all I see
is our neighbor in the doorway
hanging by his dog's choke collar.

Subway lights blind
the mind's eye. Transfers
turn the dead to distraction.

When I ride back
to where I came from,
I remember hearing
about you passing.

I thought about your dog Breezy.

A year ago you would have said
                no ma'am, no ma'am,
a hymn of the south coated in light
as she muzzled her nose out the door.

You two the same, escapist smile.

Now you say nothing
and we all wonder how
a year has gone by without you.

***

Some days I think
how easy it is to take

one more step
in front of the G
I see Patrick Phillips' poem, "Heaven."

It will be the past and we will live
there together
But there's work to be done.
The schedule still stands,
no time for twisted tea and
a myrtle afternoon.

The distance has become
too long for a phone call.

You would have loved
the shaved ice on the corner
of Bedford.

THE BORROWED SHIRT

CLAIRE CODNER

SCAN HERE!

THE BORROWED SHIRT

It all started with a yellow coat. It was bright and annoying; not quite canary yellow, but more of a bright-fucking-banana yellow that stood out like a beacon in New York City's black fashion. She was walking down the street with her oversized bag, looking up at the tops of buildings like a tourist. I knew she wasn't one by the way she walked.

That was when she noticed me noticing her. I don't blame her; after all, I had been wearing the same clothes for almost a week and had been couch surfing for roughly two months. She handed me fifty cents as she passed, and said something like, "Sorry, it's all I have right now."

I looked down at her hand and then up at her, trying to decide whether or not I should accept her misguided generosity. I laughed a little, and told her to keep it. I must have cracked a joke about knowing where my next meal was coming from, because she laughed, and a few days later we were sitting in a Starbucks together. She ordered a medium coffee and added a little cream. I ordered something with steamed milk, espresso, and chocolate syrup; brutally compromising my masculinity. I don't think I ever recovered.

Her name was Vienna, she worked with a publicist who made inappropriate comments, and loved sweets. She loved bargain bins, and her favorite movie was *Crocodile Dundee*. The original, not the two that came after, which she referred to as, "Blasphemy to true humor." I had never seen any of them at the time, so I just nodded and said, "Yeah." A few

143

months later, when I finally had, I was blown away by the impracticality of Linda Kozlowski wearing a thong bathing suit in the rough terrain of Australia, but I guess that's the '80s for you. Vienna loved it, so I learned to love it too.

Much to my mother's shock, we moved in together just over a month after I fatefully encountered her on the sidewalk, wearing her yellow coat. Over the phone, she warned me about con artists and gold diggers, to which I reminded her that I was broke and had nothing worth conning away or digging for. She was still skeptical, and proceeded to warn me about unprotected sex and rapists. My mother never liked the idea of me moving to New York. That's one of the reasons why I never told her I got mugged my first week there.

I got a filing job in a hospital. It was pretty shitty, but it helped pay the rent of our tiny white-walled apartment, which had a glorious view of an alley. Vienna tried to spruce it up with movie posters and fun throw pillows with colorful stripes that modernists might call "artsy." They reminded me of spring, but I knew that in a few decades they would be the equivalent of those forgotten brown and orange decor pieces that were "all the rage" in the '70s. I kind of liked the brown and orange stuff you found at the Salvation Army; it smelled of an old person's attic. It reminded me of the pieces that remained from my parent's first apartment together, stuff that their parents had given to them because they couldn't afford their own furniture and bedding. My parents didn't bother sending us anything like that. My mother said, "Shipping is too expensive." *Figures*.

Vienna was listening to old rap while she cooked something in a wok. She knew every word by heart and recited in true form while she poured snow peas into the simmering oil.

"V," I said, reaching around her to grab a beer from our fridge and freezer combo made of two mini-fridges. "You could make a fortune with a mix tape."

She laughed and kissed me as I wrapped my arms around her waist. She stole my beer, and her laughter grew louder and more genuine when I was forced to get another. She was lucky I loved her, or else there would have been a beer war.

Most of that night was normal. We traded stirring the wok while watching Animal Planet, and got caught up in each other on the couch. She kissed me here and there as I took off her shirt and bra. Vienna laid back and pulled me onto her, and I soon forgot about the television and the music in the other room. I forgot about being mugged my first week in New York, and how impossible my mother was. The only thing I could focus on was Vienna's soft skin and warm lips, and even when the fire alarm began to beep in the kitchen, I could focus on nothing else.

But Vienna could. She leapt from beneath me, breasts bouncing as she ran into the kitchen to remove the wok and fan the smoke away from the detector. I was suddenly aware again, and scrambled to my feet, buttoning my pants back up to join her in the kitchen. She was laughing, naked from the waist up and flushed with adrenaline when I slid into the kitchen in my socks. The smoke was thick, even though there was no fire.

"Well," Vienna said as she fanned herself. "Soup's up. Will you open the window?"

I was still panicking a little on the inside as I went to the window in the living room. She was still laughing, so I tried not to channel my mother and explode into a fit of lessons learned. I quietly pulled our makeshift blanket-curtain to the side and opened the old window that looked out onto the alley. I sucked in the fresh air, trying to cool down and calm the fast-paced beating of my heart. Soon V was next to me, giggling. "Are you okay?" she asked, rubbing her fingers against my arm. I nodded, tilting my head so it was resting on her shoulder, still shirtless, though she'd managed to find her bra.

Vienna gave my forehead a soft kiss, and I could feel my heart settling into its normal routine again. We were quiet for a while, just holding each other, until Vienna nudged me and said, "Hey, look." She smiled. "Down there."

I looked down from the window and saw two guys in the alley. They were close, and from above it looked as if they were kissing. Vienna giggled, gazing down to see the two lovers in the thralls of passion. They sure were moving a lot. Maybe too much for a make out session, but then again, what did I know of back alley love?

V kissed my cheek, commenting on how romantic it was before she made to move away from the window. That's when it happened. The two men separated, one pushing the other down before pulling out a knife and hacking at the other. I grabbed Vienna's arm. She looked down, and out of instinct yelled out a powerful, "Fuck!" into the night.

We called the police, but it felt like forever before they arrived. Meanwhile, I locked the windows and doors, and checked the perimeter of the apartment. I even checked the closet, just in case.

Vienna answered all the questions the police had for us, still in her bra, nearly hysterical. They were good sports about it, and I fought back my jealousy when one of them smiled at her. I knew he was looking at her chest and that polka-dotted bra. My answers to his questions were to the point. I had to show him who the man of the house was.

"Do you think he saw us?" V whispered after the police had left, holding the wok at the ready, now empty of any food. "Is he after us?"

"I'm not sure if he saw us, but he definitely heard us," I grumbled, glancing out of the window to see the red and blue lights flashing below.

The wok was quickly becoming a permanent fixture. One she refused to put down until the murderer was caught and prosecuted.

"Vienna." I fixed the makeshift curtain back over the window, thinking about how it resembled a Mexican blanket. What were those called? "The police said they were going to take care of it. We are fine."

"*Fine? Just fine?*" Vienna was still whispering, but it was loud in the quiet of the apartment Not discreet at all. "What if our apartment is broken into? Will we be *fine* then?"

Nothing I said to her made her put that wok down. She brought it to bed with us. She fell asleep quickly, but I was still and alert for what seemed like hours. My body felt heavy against the mattress, so drowsy from sleepiness that my muscles ached, but my mind kept replaying the stabbing in my head. I could even hear the noise it made, soft and blunt. On top of that, my mom's voice kept screaming in my ear, "*You'll lose all your money and get raped and murdered in a dark alley!*" For once I thought that maybe, just *maybe*, she could be right. Maybe.

Maybe not.

V sometimes snored in her sleep, and that night she did. It was a breathy snore through her open mouth, and was both adorable and annoying. I thought about waking her up and finishing what we started on the couch earlier, but I knew the wok was her bed companion for the night, and I didn't want to risk it colliding with my face. I stared at the ceiling, trying to ignore my mother's voice in my head. She'd based her opinions of New York on movies and the news, which never reported anything but tragedy or adorable children doing helpful things. Unfortunately for me, the adorable children never lived in the city.

I startled awake suddenly. My muscles tensed, and my heart jumped into full throttle. I must have just fallen asleep, but I had no idea what had made me twitch like that. Nightmares about my mother seemed reasonable, but then I heard

147

the loud knocking from the living room. I stiffened painfully, and held my breath so I wouldn't give away my position.

The knocking kept coming, so I finally inched out of bed and walked carefully from the bedroom to the front door. The knocking continued.

"Who is it?" I put my eye to the peephole. The hall outside was dark and bent out of shape from the fishbowl lens I was looking through. A dark, tall man stood in the hall, looking as if he had stepped out of the '40s with his trench coat and hat. "Detective Bishop," he said.

I was satisfied with that answer, and undid the locks and chain on the door, opening it enough to get a look at Detective Bishop and then enough for him to come in. "I'm sorry," he said in a monotone fashion, taking smooth, quick steps into the apartment. "I know it is late."

I offered him coffee; he politely declined. I asked him what this was about; he reached into his pocket. I waited to see a badge or a pad of paper to take notes on, but all I saw was the wok swinging through the air and beating Detective Bishop over the head. He fell forward onto me.

"Vienna!" I yelled. She screamed. I lowered Detective Bishop down on the floor. Vienna jumped up and down, still screaming, wok in hand. "He had a gun!"

"He's a cop!"

"A cop?"

"*A cop!*"

"A *cop!*" she screamed.

No pulse. No breath. No movement. A dead cop.

***

The cabby didn't ask questions when we pulled our drunk friend into the back seat and said, "11th and 12th, please." Vienna, still shaking, clutched her oversized bag to her chest.

148

She tried speaking to me, but I didn't hear her. I was counting the street numbers as they moved by. The driver was too slow. Our friend sat between us, his head leaning against my shoulder. Each turn made him move, and I had to keep him still so that he wouldn't fall forward. I had let him borrow the Hawaiian shirt my dad got me on his trip to Massachusetts.

"That's where *Jaws* was filmed," V told me after it arrived. I told her she was wrong, but she was right, and I hated that stupid shirt. It had arrived shortly after we had moved in together with a note from my mother that said: *Your father has been waiting for you to have a real address to send this to you.*

That had been it, that and the shirt, which was an appalling spray of purple and yellow flowers. I'd pushed it into the dresser and forgot about it. Vienna laughed and told me not to worry. They would understand someday, even if it didn't feel like it. She always had a way of making me feel better.

We had only fought once, and I almost walked out on her. I hopped on the train to Penn Station and, even though I had very little money, almost bought a ticket to Albany on the Amtrak. I stood in the station looking at the departures for a half hour, and then I turned around and went home. She'd seen an old boyfriend, and I had let my imagination run wild. I accused her of having an affair, which I later regretted when I saw her crying. I had promised myself that night that I would never leave her again.

I paid and tipped the cabby. Not too much and not too little. I didn't want him to remember us, but I did feel bad about transporting a dead body in his cab. Vienna was visibly nervous as she jumped from the car, still clutching her bag, and whispered for me to hurry. Detective Bishop was heavy.

We lugged him down the bike path, propped up between us, slowly walking past the construction yard and toward the park. There were a few clusters of people out, but they stayed to the benches and grass. We moved toward the water.

149

She tried whispering again, "In the cab I thought I saw him blink!"

"He didn't," I said, adjusting Detective Bishop beneath my arm. "He's dead."

"Are you sure? I think he's breathing."

"Make sure no one is looking." I looked down at his body. He wasn't moving. We both looked at his chest, but it was still. Detective Bishop was stone cold dead.

When we reached the water, I lifted him up by his shoulders, hooking my arms under his and pulling. "Grab his feet," I said, and Vienna nervously obeyed. "Wesley, remember that movie? The one about the old men who killed a girl? They thought she was dead, but she wasn't, and the memory haunted them!"

"*Ghost Story*," I grunted as we lifted the cop over the railing and dangled him above the dark, inky water. "That was a book first."

"I know," she whispered, looking behind us at the groups of people, not too far off. We couldn't tell if they were looking our way or not. "But what if he's not dead?"

"Trust me," I said as I tried to support his upper body, and she let his feet drop. They swung for a moment, only inches from the water now, supported by nothing but my tired arms. I began to gently lower him down into the black.

"I heard there were sharks in here," Vienna said, grabbing onto Detective Bishop's left arm. "Don't drop him!"

I thought about the shirt. "You mean *Jaws* sharks?"

"No. Small ones."

"All sharks are small compared to Jaws."

"Yeah, but these ones are actually small," she explained. "Or at least I heard they were."

We gently submerged the rest of him into the water, and watched as he disappeared below the dock. I looked down for a moment, expecting him to float back up like a bad dream. I knew that he would eventually surface somewhere, unless a shark got to him first.

"Okay." I took a heavy breath. "The bag, now."

Vienna reached into the oversized canvas bag and pulled out a black trash bag. Inside were Detective Bishop's business clothes and personal effects, and also the wok, which we figured would act as an anchor.

She dangled the bag over the railing and leaned as close to the water as she could to avoid a loud splash. Once it sank, we stood there for a moment. "Do you think we should say something?" I asked quietly.

"Yeah." She pouted. "I'm gonna miss that wok."

***

The next few days made me jittery. I jumped whenever a car passed, which, seeing as I lived in New York City, quickly became a problem. Vienna even noticed my nerves. I told her I had been drinking a lot of caffeine, but I think we both knew it was because I couldn't stop thinking about Detective Bishop. I had dreams that I was drowning. I woke up after hearing pounding on the door in my dreams.

I was sitting on the couch when V came home with a new wok. I stared at it for a good fifteen minutes, just sitting there on the counter, taunting me. That wok hated me. She began to cook, switching on her rap music and shaking her hips back and forth as she opened a beer. "Want one?" she called to me.

My eye twitched. "No," I said calmly, still staring at the wok. "What are you cooking?"

"Noodles," she said. "Lots and lots of noodles. Delicious noodles." Her noodles were my favorite. She liked to put chunks of garlic in the oil before browning the chicken and making a mixture of soy sauce and cornstarch. That was the first thing she ever cooked me, and that was when I told her I

151

loved her. Never before had I felt so strongly about a woman.

I watched her hips rock as she stood at the stove. They reminded me of the waves at the piers. "V," I said quietly, and she turned around mid-swig of her bottle.

"Did you really see him blink in the cab?"

We looked at each other for a minute, but then she smiled. "No." She laughed. "I was just nervous and seeing things." Another minute passed, and it was my turn to speak. "Yeah, but you said…"

"No, Wesley. He's dead."

"But you also saw him breathing!"

Vienna shrugged. "We both saw that he wasn't, Wess. Don't worry about it." She turned back to the noodles.

"What if we killed him?"

Vienna looked uncomfortable. This was the first time we had talked about it so openly. "Wesley, either way, we killed him."

I had never killed before. Well, nothing big anyway. Once, I hit a deer with my dad's truck upstate. It was night, and I was fresh on my license. I thought I was so cool driving around by myself, listening to music and singing along to the chorus because I didn't know all the words. I had been making a turn, one of those turns that never end and just keep revealing more and more curved stretches of highway.

That's when the deer rushed out in front of me. It smacked the front of the truck so hard its hoof came through the windshield and my back wheels lifted off the ground for a second.

I never had nightmares about it, though. I never woke up hearing the crush of metal against bone. I never thought about what it was like to be hit by that truck.

"Hey," I said, and V turned her head to listen. "Doesn't that book *Ghost Story* take place upstate?"

"Parts of it, I think," she said, stirring the noodles.

"Maybe we should move upstate."

BRUGADA

NICOLAS AMARA

BRUGADA

I should've reacted more quickly, he thought to himself, there's no way for certain, but certainly, no, yes, he did that so that we would stop and the three of them could take her clothes off with their eyes, there was nothing funny or playful about it. Everyone has a case that they're trying to move from their brain over into reality, and they'll do anything to manifest it. The next thing I know, if we didn't move on from that spot, they'd be pushing me back and forth, and one of them would grab her. The tension was thick enough to be felt in those few seconds, in that jeering smile, he thought, I would've fought them but I couldn't have and would never have. I can see the saliva forming in the corners of their mouths. No, he thought, I wouldn't have been able to. But if given the chance I would've shot them all. Yes, if I could have killed them all, I wouldn't discern between responsibilities. I would've finally judged. I would've lined them up and put a bullet in each of their skulls.

***

He stopped in front of him. His friends sat close by on a park bench. She stopped shortly behind him. They watched from their seats.

A silence passed. He looked him onto the ground.

They kept on walking, she catching up to him.

157

***

Later that day he mowed the lawn, pushing and pulling back and forth, under the apple tree and pear trees. He made sure to cover every single inch of the lawn with the mower lest that individual spot began to grow unruly in its own way. There was no room for hesitation here; every blade should be mowed down immediately and indiscernibly. He kept on mowing into the field and over each and every bump, moving the mower back and forth over these bumps to make sure everything was gone and leveled and uncurious.

When he finished, he was very thirsty. He went inside and poured a glass of water, watching the air rise in the glass. He also watched the ants. One by one, they made their way from the hole in the wall, crawling onward toward the sink. Crumbs of bread and other food were stuck in the drain catcher. They marched down into the metal basin to retrieve them. He watched them from above. He admired their determination, but his wrists became rigid. He ended each of their lives in asphyxiation. One by one, the ants that escaped saw their comrades killed in action by a god whose pleasure it was to dislocate the thorax from the head. Their legs lay scattered across the side of the sink. How nice it might be, he thought, to kill each and every person who walked past me, to know their final end was a determination of mine and truly existed in my life, blotting the timeline of my days with eventful beginnings and endings; because each ending truly is a new beginning, and I will hurt myself later for succumbing to such expected sayings so that I remember and am made, but one day is not a day unless it is marked with an event. And what event has more gravity than this? Each tiny moment pushed to the brink by my index finger. We otherwise wander or sit in the same circle, barraged by unrelenting rays of sun and the voices of children at play. How I want to cut out each of their

158

tongues and spit in their bleeding faces.

Someone knocked at the door.

***

"I've come to collect," he said.

He looked on at him through the porthole. He did not speak.

The man on the dock looked about himself, making sure his buttons were buttoned right before speaking again. "I've come to collect," he repeated.

But who hasn't? he thought.

His house began to rock.

***

Later on that night he sat in his kitchen drinking a cup of coffee. The cup was old, as was the coffee—approximately three days. The shutters on the kitchen window were still with age.

I do not turn on the coffee maker, he thinks, no. I do not place my outlines near any foreign lands.

The kitchen went on, as did the house, paused.

She, on the other side of town, sat idly on the sofa of a friend, talking vaguely about politics and local gossip, sipping on the drink that had been opened for her upon arrival. The music played with the smoke, drifting lengthwise across the space. The circle of friends arranged themselves toward the door. She sat in the corner by the stereo.

The kitchen released itself as he sighed, "I hope she feels this," peeling the paint from his eyelids.

***

The paunch scent of pine was not unlike any other paunch

smell had on any given morning, nor would one be surprised if they were to unfold a piece of paper and, expecting a note, find a little drab piece of thread, shredded at each end.

He spread the butter on his morning toast. The sky rocked awfully today. He smoothed the butter with slow, steady strokes of the butter knife.

This is a day for fishing, he thought, and nearly wept. He concentrated on the lines of the sky from the porthole above the sink. Outside, the sun was only just rising as he looked out at it, making sure that it was. His senses rifled through his body three times before he picked a sedate one.

The birds aren't quite as observant as you'd think they were, no, in fact they possess no power of will and are only governed by sudden indulgence, yes, if I were to possess one bird, no, I would not dare to sever such ties with the corporal.

She, on the other hand, thought greatly of this freedom, and yet, here we were, cemented with soggy guilt to a gold carpet, picking out the filings of her nails from her face, severed with teeth the night before. Yes, here we are, they affirm.

One of few things they receive and declare together.

The grass cut yesterday remains where it had fallen, coagulating in small islands on the ground. It is not unsurprising either that the dishwasher talks in its sleep.

***

Often walking away from the subject can give one the renewed confidence to confront a number of other devices. Giving said devices any indication provides them with life, and leaves a number of holes.

She having gotten out of work early knew that she wanted to remember what had happened the previous night and wanted to be able to arrive home and call him on the phone and let him know precisely what had happened lest she forget because without telling where would all of the moments go.

God bless you, a man without a pant leg called from behind her as she walked down a street.

We're going to suppose a lot of things today. This is the only way we are going to get through.

We are going to understand very little and, instead, confront every feeling that boils up in us and break their bubbles like reptile eggs.

***

If I wanted to shoot you...No, I do and have always wanted to shoot you. I have wanted to stick the barrel up into the crevice under your eyelid and blow the scalp off of your skull since the day was young.

This, he believes, is how he will confront anyone he might meet lest he leave his home on this day. He might live in the body of a cold and bitter cloud. The petals on all of these flowers reply with similar walls.

There are some things we can do without, like fingernails. Hair dye we cannot. Lysol we cannot. Gravity we cannot. Broken glass we cannot. Blood plus pieces of cellophane plus capitals and social signifiers we will forfeit under most circumstances.

***

I find out that there is little else to say except for the straight line which juts out past my face, leaving the lateral intersections to speak for something yet unknown but still never knowable, for what has been spoken that can in fact finally nail down the essence of the unknown.

We listen to the dryer whirr on loop for days before we take our sleeping heads from our ovens and open the door outside. Too many loops forward make questions unanswerable. If we cut all of the loops we can maintain this stasis.

I measure melted barbed wire in a paper cup. The mixture hardens into something, feels like a substance holding weight, but not sharp, perhaps round. How do we measure liquid? Only two ways to go back.

Outside is only our conception of everything as framed by something. Once we skew ourselves into a nothing, we have found a new space.

The ground says and says and says and...

***

The kitchen went on, as did the house...
...we breathe in ellipsis, we quantify something...
in the spaces...shhh...
If he traces the line to the door and we undo the lock, we therefore are able to forfeit his right of structural input from there on out, and if this is all spliced together, maybe we can will ourselves to erase the whole mess permanently.

Nothing more dangerous than wanting to nail down the world in paralysis and not giving a fuck where anything goes afterward.

***

After he had dressed, pulled on the underwear he had stolen from the women's section at Goodwill, peeled off his pinky fingernail and painted the rest blue, slipped into an old sweatshirt and jeans worn dry and flaked from dock building, he left the boat. Two and a half miles into town at a walking pace meant that he'd be knocking on the door of her house at sundown, winding up to put the barrel through the porthole of the door. This was something more honest than God, more willed than any shit he had taken in the past forty-three years. She was a happy-go-lucky type, a cheerleader from high school learning to live with a wrinkled old skin, pole dancing by night and putting the cold side of a five into the grisly hand at dawn. But she loved to talk and carry on, sit on the bar stool until its age willed her off for her bashfulness. The barman closed the bar and let her sleep there if she hadn't left yet, put her down under the bar with a blanket and bottle to keep her quiet. We didn't think anything of it if we'd seen it from afar; we might keep living on any way that we wanted. But he couldn't remember now what the face of her face looked like. When she talked over him he reeled into himself and sealed off like a clam. How could anyone be so sure of themselves? Without even the partial dip into a massive action? Just a quarrel to pass the time; bickering to break the bricks of her world. I've tried and I've carved something quantifiable, my world, my way, and yet…The time passes irreversibly and there is no thing that I can name as my own. No, not one piece of rope attached to any one oar.

He walked with steady even steps, making sure not to miss one plank of the dock as he made his way. This was how they all did it, every single human being in the past and in the future, put their feet down one by one, creating a lineage and history, making sure not to let any substantial motion slip through the cracks.

He felt the lace of his panties ride up into the crevice of his ass, and he thought, and he thought…Still, nothing stuck.

The thinking is what counts. That's what they tell you in all of these books. In the end, the thinking and putting down and making is what makes a person sane. To try and figure out your world, that's what makes reality in the end; in the end, after we've all danced into some box, after we're all shot down and dead.

GETTING THERE

TESS MANGIARDI

GETTING THERE

The cab dropped me off at nine p.m. the night before.

It was the first time I had seen the house in a year. Illuminated by a single light, it wasn't the home that I remembered. The two large rectangular windows that had once seemed alive with light now bleak, the front door suffocating from the darkness in a way that made it seem as if it were frowning. A hand pulled the curtain, followed by a tall pretty frame and a smile.

My mother.

I'd half expected to come home and be flooded with family. That's the way it used to be. Instead, it was just her waving to me from the window.

My mother in her pearls and her black suit.

She was jumping up and down, flailing her arms, before closing the curtain. My eyes traced her shadow rushing to the front door.

"Ma'am? Sixty dollars?"

The cab driver was looking back at me, his unibrow furrowed and bushy.

"Oh, right, I'm sorry."

He grunted, taking my crumpled bills and throwing them in the passenger seat. I got out of the car. He didn't help me with my bags.

I stood, my feet planted firmly on the sidewalk as he drove away, struck by the silence—the only sound for miles was a symphony of tree frogs. I took a breath and walked slowly up the driveway.

The last time I had set foot here, mascara streaked my face and I was wearing two different shoes. There had been people gathered on the lawn, staring at me with wide-eyed pity as I felt for the first time the kind of numbness that I would soon get used to. With my suitcases in hand, clothes stuck in the zippers, I had walked past all of them with my head down and promised myself I'd never look back.

Yet here I was.

And there she was, smiling down at me from the open door.

"Fina! Fina! Fina!"

She had lipstick on her teeth.

"Hi, Mom."

"Oh my god! You're finally here!"

I opened my mouth in response, but she continued, "Let me take your bags. Was the flight okay? The cab ride? Meet anyone new? Your hair is a mess!"

She smoothed the side of my hair before I could get a chance to respond and took me into a tight embrace, my arms reluctant to wrap around her. She was treating my visit as if it was just like any other. It hadn't even been a minute, and I already felt that familiar sting in my chest. I had imagined this moment the entire flight, thinking that maybe my mother had changed. That she'd greet me with a somber touch, and I daydreamed about reconciliation. Of course, daydreams are daydreams for a reason. When I saw her wide smile and eyes coated with denial—there was anger. So much anger, and I wasn't sure what I had expected. Reconciliation seemed overrated anyway. She smoothed down my hair again, and I wanted to tell her to stop touching me. There was so much I wanted to say. Instead, I painted on a smile. The flight had been a long one. I was too tired to be fighting already.

"I forgot how expensive cabs are here," I said.

She ushered me in with a laugh.

"Well, honey, this isn't New York."

"Definitely not."

I tried not to notice the clunky GPS tracker wrapped around her ankle. I'd watched a million episodes of Law and Order, as if that was supposed to prepare me for how big it was. It had a green light on it, blinking to a rhythm I couldn't understand—I didn't think it would be so bright. As she walked ahead of me, I noted how strange it looked paired with her black Louboutins.

The inside of the house was just as it always had been, clean and perfectly pristine, no file cabinets lying on the floor, the couch tidy instead of overturned.

"It looks so nice in here," I said.

"Oh, Fina, when has it ever *not* looked nice."

I didn't say a word.

***

"Mom? Where is all my stuff?"

Red in my chest. Already. Still.

"What? What do you mean your stuff?"

"Um, my clothes, my books, my *bed*!"

"Oh, the sub-letters are coming next week, so that's all in storage."

Nausea. Throughout my life "storage" was on par with the tooth fairy or Santa Clause–fiction. The room that had been my solace from the world, where I had gotten my first kiss, my escape, now looked like a hospital room. White on white. Bookshelves empty. Single bed. Metal frame. I hadn't realized how badly I'd miss it until I couldn't come back to it anymore. There was nothing left. The slate clean. I couldn't believe it. I couldn't fucking believe it.

"Oh my god. Why didn't you just leave my stuff with

someone? The landlord? I could have come a few days early to come get it—"

"You'll get it all back in a few years."

Lie.

"Yeah? Then why don't you give me the address and I'll go get it myself. Or we could go now."

I heard her sigh from the other room. We were yelling through the walls.

"You know I can't leave past eight in the evening, dear."

"Mom! My stuff, my books! My first edition of Hemingway."

"Oh, honey, it's just stuff. Don't be a brat."

"Just stuff? It was mine! I was excited to take it with—"

She cut me off. I heard her coming down the hallway.

"I saved this for you. I thought you'd want to take it home."

She opened the door, ignoring my rage, holding a golden frame. I took it from her, my jaw tight. It was a picture of her and I from when we went to Paris. I was five and we were both wearing stripes. It used to be my favorite picture because our smiles looked identical, and we looked so happy. Under it, my mom had scrawled the words, "Me and My Mini-Me" in her chunky handwriting. My stomach clenched. I wanted nothing to do with that stupid picture. I had loved it and her so much, and I didn't want to feel that anymore.

"Out of everything, and *this* is what you save?"

She opened her mouth in protest, but closed it and bit her lip.

"You don't have to keep it, Fina. Anyway," she continued, "I got Steven to buy us some groceries for tonight. Thought we could cook."

"So you can get the landlord to buy you groceries, but you couldn't get him to keep a few fuc—" I took a breath. "A few boxes?"

A look.

"I'll be in the kitchen when you're ready, Fina."

She turned around then, walked down the hallway, descending the stairs with quiet steps.

I put my suitcase in the corner, not even bothering to unpack, and sat on the bed for a moment. I mourned the possessions that were probably sitting in boxes at a Goodwill or on a landfill somewhere. It wasn't the loss of the things themselves—not really. It was just yet another piece gone from my previous life, another lie tangling with the rest of them. The façade of her perfection had already shattered, and now it seemed as if there were no pieces left to repair it with.

"Hurry up! I'm so hungry!"

"'Kay, all right, I'm coming," I shouted.

My mother stood in the kitchen. She was wearing a ridiculous yellow apron, her hair up, lipstick off. The kitchen was bare, all the decorations and photographs that once lined the walls just empty frames catching shadows.

"What're we having?"

"Your favorite!"

"Chicken parm?"

"You know it!"

"Wouldn't it be easier to just order in?"

"Fina, come on. You used to love cooking with me."

I looked at her, at her big brown eyes pleading with me. I was supposed to be there to take care of her. I was supposed to support her and cook for her, despite everything she'd done. I was supposed to forget.

I melted butter in a pan, listening to it sizzle. She watched me eagerly. It was as though she thought cooking would fix everything, erase the fact that I had barely spoken to her or that it'd been a month since I had taken any of her calls. Maybe she thought it would put us back together again, but no matter what delusional idea she had come up with before I arrived, it would take so much more than a few ingredients to fix what was broken. There was no place here for daydreams

"So, Steven bought these groceries?"

"Oh, yeah. He's been a real big help in all this mess. Buy me groceries. Drove me to my lawyer a few times. You know that kind of stuff."

"Weird. Well, he has always been in love with you."

Stir. Season. Repeat.

"Yeah, I guess that turned out to work in my favor. I'm glad to have him around. It's been lonely here."

I didn't reply.

"He's even letting us take that silly car tomorrow."

"Who is?"

"Steven, honey."

"The yellow Beetle?"

"I know! Won't it be funny? Us tall girls in that little thing."

It was the first time either of us had mentioned the drive.

She babbled on, trying to find a way to fill the silence the way the smell of food filled the kitchen. She was being polite.

I bit my tongue, thinking about the way that things had been before.

My mom was my best friend when I was a kid. In kindergarten, I brought her to show and tell, convincing everyone in my class that she was a fairy princess in disguise. The class had oooh-ed and ahhh-ed as I forced her to hold a wand that I had crafted out of construction paper the day before. She was smiling down at me, red lips on white teeth, moving the wand above my head as I twirled round and round, throwing glitter in the air and giggling with the rest of the class. Back then, I was the little girl in the pigtails and poofy dresses and she was my fairy princess.

Then I grew up, became a teenager, stopped believing in fairies. My mom went from a celestial being to just my mother, the woman who wore Chanel suits to PTA meetings, who insisted on taking our laundry to be dry-cleaned despite having a working washer and dryer. There were days when I wished she were like the other moms, the ones who sometimes picked my friends up in scrunchies and sweatpants. My mother wouldn't even let anyone see her without lipstick. Yet, I admired her beauty, her ability to walk into any room and light it up. I had wanted to be just like her. Back then, I looked up to her because she still found a way to be everything.

Now, though, I looked at her long brown hair, slicked back into a tight bun, her skinny face, and saw nothing but the wrinkles pulling at her eyes.

When the food was finished, we sat down to eat. My mother stared at her plate and I stared at mine, and I wondered how we'd survive this trip ahead of us without losing our minds. I wondered if she was thinking the same thing.

Afterward, we did the dishes. We went to sleep. We didn't talk.

The two of us had mastered the art of saying so much without ever having to say anything at all.

***

The next morning, we were already fighting.

"Mom, you know, maybe it would be better if we just took all this stuff out."

I struggled and heaved, exhausted and not yet awake, trying to get my giant suitcase into the back of the landlord's 1970 Volkswagen Beetle. It was cluttered with Steven's stuff.

My mother stood behind me, her little black bag grasped tightly in her hands. She sighed as she watched me push and pull, grunt and groan. The cool morning breeze wrapped around my legs, my skirt hiking up to my thighs.

"No, Fina. It's not ours to move. It'll fit."

She tapped her foot lightly on the concrete.

"Well, fine then, Mom. You do it."

She smirked and placed her bag on the roof of the car, putting a precise hand on my hips and pushing me over with a click of her tongue.

"Everything has a system. It's like I never taught you anything."

She took the suitcase in her hands, lifted it up, and placed it in the trunk. It fit perfectly. She looked up at me, satisfied. I rolled my eyes.

"And pull down that skirt, honey. You look like a hoochie."

I watched her walk to the passenger side of the car with disdain and pulled my cotton skirt down to my knees. I looked back at the house, realizing that I was looking at it for the last time. It wasn't the same house that had held so much happiness during my childhood. I had already said goodbye to that house. This one was just empty.

When I got into the car, my mother sat with her eyes fixed ahead, blinking rapidly into the newly risen sun.

We drove slowly down the road, and that first hour was spent without a word. Her naked fingernails tap, tap, tapped away on the corner of her seat. I had never seen her nails unpainted. I cleared my throat, gripping the steering wheel so hard it hurt.

I saw her look at me from the corner of my eye. One of her piercing stares. She looked as if she was about to say something, but chose not to. She seemed tired. I was beginning to notice that every little thing she did seemed tired.

I flicked on the radio. She turned it off.

We drove another half hour with just her tapping fingers as the soundtrack.

***

My mother and I started taking spontaneous road trips whenever I came down to visit from college. It seemed like

174

something she would never do, but she became obsessed with making it a tradition. I never questioned it. She was good at making sure I never questioned it.

I'd fly in, we'd spend a day or two with family, and then we would stuff the car with snacks and blankets and all of our favorite CDs. We'd spend hours in that car, but we never knew where we were going. We just got on the highway and drove. Or, I used to think we never knew. I found out later that she always did, that the road trips were part of it. The "random" people we met along the way were part of it too. I would ask my mom where we were headed, and she would always laugh and say, "Honey, it's never about the destination. It's all about getting there."

Getting there.

I thought about the words as we drove in silence. They had a new meaning now. This time we were going to prison. My mother was. And I was dropping her off. No one else had wanted to do it. Even the landlord had his limits. I was the only one she had left.

My mother was a workaholic. When I was in high school, I'd listen to her sit in her office and chatter away, often laughing pleasantly at her desk. It was only as I got older that I noticed her constant laughter was frequently exploding into screams. By the time I was in college, she'd begun to keep her phone off. She bought a deadbolt for her doors. She kept the blinds closed shut.

They called it a white-collar crime. My mother called it a mistake.

I felt a slight pain in my chest. All I had to do was get her there.

"Fina?"

"Mhm?"

"Do you still love me at all?"

My vision blurred. I wanted to stop the car and throw her

out. Tell her to walk. To find her own way there. After everything she'd done, she had the audacity to ask if I still loved her.

"I'm driving you to this goddamn place, aren't I?"

"Watch your language! You, just, you know, it wasn't my fault. Do you think it was all my fault?"

"Are you kidding me, Mom? Are you really asking me that question right now?"

"Well, you know, I couldn't pay them back. And they attacked me. I just want to make sure you know that."

"What the hell are you talking about? Oh my god. I can't even believe you right now!"

My knuckles turned white.

"You just never came to visit—"

"Seriously, Mom? I never came to visit because—" I sighed. "You know why I didn't come. You know."

"No, I don't. We were so close before, and then I don't know what happened."

"Are you kidding me? You cannot be that delusional."

A moment past. "But, do you still love me?"

"Would I be driving you here if I didn't?"

She looked out the window, her eyes searching for something. Maybe a way out. I didn't know. I didn't care.

I wanted more than anything to be sitting next to the mother that I had known my entire life. The one who always had the answer. The one I knew before I ever learnt about eviction notices, bad debt, negative balances. My mother could enchant anyone around her, but it was all a lie. A mirage. For years, I believed in trips that never came, money that was never spent, clothes we'd never buy. Year after year, I kept believing. I believed every word that came out of her mouth because I believed that she had it all. And maybe she did once.

Now, though, all she had to her name was a little black purse. Pearls. And Me.

We drove on, my heart aching, anxiety rising and falling like waves.

My mom was itching at her tracker, the black band etching deep red scratches against her skin. I looked at the remnants of my tan and wondered when she last laid out in the sun. We used to lie out together, her in a big floppy sunhat slathered in pounds of sunblock. She'd always tell me the same anecdote about how sunblock kept her young. Now, her skin seemed worn, ghostly.

"I'm hungry," she said suddenly.

I couldn't look at her.

"Me, too. Want to stop?"

"Yeah, I'm so hungry I could eat just about anything," she said.

We ended up finding a Waffle House. "Like old times," my mother said. "Pecan waffles!" She tried to smile, and so did I. After all, we had always been good at pretending.

My mom entered the Waffle House in her black dress suit and pearls, acting as if she was walking into the fanciest restaurant in the world.

"Does this tracker make me look fat?" she asked in a whisper, pointing down at her ankle. I wanted to laugh, but I couldn't. How could I have laughed?

I said nothing.

Inside was quiet. The seats were faded like acid washed jeans, the black and white checkered floor stained with syrup and the kind of grime unique to southern freeways.

The woman behind the counter and a tall cook greeted us with smiles that had the equivalent of one full set of teeth. They looked like redneck bumblebees.

"Welcome to Waffle House, y'all. Make yourself comfortable."

"Well hey there, guys!" my mom said with a southern twang I'd never heard before. Her smile was wide. "Isn't this

177

just the nicest Waffle House I've ever seen!"

They erupted with laughter, my mother's charm hitting them like a virus, infecting them with love for a woman they didn't even know. The waitress nodded at me. It was this nod of recognition, almost like pride, something that said, "Aren't you proud to be related to *her*?" And I used to be. God, I really used to be.

My mom slid down into an open booth, me across from her. Before we even got a chance to really look at the menu, the woman came up to us, her face red, sweat at her temples. She was smiling excitedly, as if she was taking the order of a celebrity. My mother had said all of two sentences to this woman and she was already fawning over her. I wondered how the hell she did it. I smiled up at the waitress, ignored, watching my mother wink at the woman as if they'd just shared a secret.

"Hey, y'all, my name is Bertha! What can ayegetcha two ladies today?"

"Bertha! We were just so excited to come to the Waffle House today. My daughter just flew here all the way from New York City!"

Against my own will, I wanted to say.

Bertha gasped. "New York City! Well, bless your heart, coming here to be with your Mama! I could have sworn you two were sisters, you two look so alike."

"Oh stop!" my mom said, pleased. She squeezed Bertha's arm and then looked over at me. "Yep! That's my Mini-Me."

They looked at me as if I was on display at a museum, and I feigned a smile. I tried to be a part of the show—If I didn't, the waitress would take my mother's side and I'd be the enemy. I was so tired of playing along, but I was too wary not to.

"Well, what can ayegetcha two ladies to eat?"

"One pecan waffle, with butter from the grill melted on top," my mom said, winking again. "And, Oh! A side of grits.

Extra butter on that, too."

"And for you?"

"Uh, I'll have the same. Just, no grits. Hash browns. Cheese."

"You don't like grits?" my mom asked, staring at me as if I'd offended her.

"I've never liked grits, Mom."

"Oh."

"It's like you don't even know me at all."

She shot me a look and smiled at the woman.

Bertha didn't notice, too caught up in my mother.

"That'll be all?"

"Two coffees," I said.

"Please," my mother added.

Bertha walked off and my mother dropped her smile.

We stared at each other. "How long do we have left?" she asked eventually.

"It's at the next exit."

"The hotel or the…other place?" She didn't want to say it.

"The hotel. Not the prison."

She flinched, and I felt good about making her flinch.

My mom fiddled with her knife and fork, inspecting them for smudges. She looked up suddenly, smiling at me with feigned excitement.

"Well, this will be a good last dinner, right?"

"You sound like you're dying."

"Might as well be. I don't know if there will be waffles as good as this there."

"I don't know." I shrugged. "I've never been to prison."

She flushed. "I wish you'd stop saying that so loud, Fina."

"I'm just saying where we're going." There was no point in sugarcoating it.

"Well, stop it." She looked embarrassed. "Tell me what's new," she said after a while. "Any new boyfriends? How's

179

work?"

"No new boyfriends. Work is fine."

I clenched a fork in my hand. My heart ached. She was still performing. I was just waiting for the curtain call.

"Come on, honey. Please?" She was looking at me pleadingly.

"Yeah, well. There's this one guy. He's all right, kind of distant."

The truth was I had met someone, and he was wonderful—at first. He had loved me, but he couldn't take the nights I woke up screaming out for my mother in cold sweats. He told me he needed a break, that my anxiety was suffocating him; I needed to deal with my problems on my own. I should have told her that, but I couldn't. I wasn't sure she deserved to know. I wasn't even sure she *wanted* to know.

"Oh, a guy! You'll have to tell me what happens. I can call once a day, you know. What else?"

I should tell her about the eviction notices, about the classes I missed because I just couldn't get myself out of bed. I should tell her about how the past year had almost killed me, how I had never felt so alone, but instead I said, "Um, the friends are doing well. I've been seeing a therapist. Thinking about moving soon."

"You've been seeing a therapist? For how long?"

"Six months," I said, watching her jaw clench and her eyes open wide.

"Oh, honey, why in the world would you need a therapist?" She paused, and reached out for Bertha, "Excuse me? Hi, darling. Can you get me a cup of 180-degree water, please? I want to dip my silverware in it. It's dirty."

"Of course, honey. One second."

I felt anger rise to my face as I stared at her in disbelief. Was she serious? There was a reason I hadn't come to visit in a year, and it all lay ahead of us, just a few exits away. I thought of everything she'd never told me. All the lies. The people she hurt. Bertha placed the cup of hot water in front of her. My mom picked up her knife carefully and swirled it in the glass, eyes bright and filled with denial. I wondered if there was ever any turning back.

"So, therapy? What for?"

She wiped the knife off with her napkin and picked up the spoon, putting it in the cup and spinning it round and round; it clinked against the sides. I bit my lip.

"Oh, I don't know, Mother. Probably all the issues I have to work through."

"Issues? Well, I sure hope you don't talk about me."

That was it. I felt a white hot rage exploding inside my chest. I'd spent so many years watching her be perfect, wishing I could be just like her, only for her to shatter the image that I had looked up to for years.

"Are you kidding?" I was shaking.

My mom picked her fork up and dipped it in the cup.

"Can you fucking stop sanitizing your silverware, please? Okay? Just fucking stop!"

Bertha was just bringing us our food, and her smile dropped. She stood in front of our table, maple syrup dripping over the plate onto her calloused fingers.

My mom looked at me in a way that I hoped to never be looked at by anyone. Her eyes were welling with tears, her body trembling, and worst of all, she just looked so tired. The magic had drained from her cheeks, and pale skin was all that was left. She had no more fight in her eyes. Just lipstick on her teeth.

"Well, I'm sorry I don't like germs." Her bottom lip quivered.

Bertha placed our food down on the table. She gave me a dirty look.

My mother looked so broken in that moment, small, like a

woman I'd never met before. I should have gotten up, moved to her side and held her the way she used to hold me when I was hurting. I wanted to tell her that I was sorry. That it wasn't her fault. I should have talked about what just happened. About the past year. About what had happened to our life.

Instead, I picked up my fork and began to eat.

My mom cleared her throat, looking away from me as a tear fell from her lashes. She picked up her un-sanitized fork, and her knife, cutting the golden waffles into triangles, spreading the butter, wrapping the maple syrup around the piece on her fork like spaghetti.

I watched as she brought each bite to her mouth with a trembling hand.

"It's good." Her voice was small, childlike.

"Yeah, really good."

I paid the bill, half expecting my mother to remind me to tip well. That's what she would have done before. Instead, she avoided looking at me and got up, walking toward the door, wiping syrup on her jacket.

"Have a blessed day," Bertha called after us. Neither of us looked up. Neither of us said goodbye.

"Are we still going to the hotel?" my mom asked, quiet, after we'd gotten back in the car.

"That's the plan."

"Oh, good. That'll be nice, right? One last lap of luxury?"

The way her voice sounded, as if we were going on an extended vacation. She insisted on pretending, as if the Waffle House or discussions of therapists was a thing of fiction. The small, pitiful woman that I had wanted to hug before had vanished, replaced with this larger than life woman that I despised.

"Um. I wouldn't say lap of luxury, but sure."

"You're not excited?"

"Thrilled."

She looked at me and clicked her tongue.

"Why do you have to be so sarcastic all the time, Fina? Can't you just be nice to me?"

I said nothing, turned up the radio, and get off the next exit. At least we weren't hungry anymore.

***

The hotel was settled in a mass expanse of golf course greenery, the extravagance of the building towering over the palm trees. It was massive, painted two different shades of white, surrounded by nothing but miles of green.

"Park valet, dear. The parking lot is too far and my heels hurt."

"Do you have money for that? Because I'm already paying for gas and food and—"

"Don't be so dramatic, Fina. You know they're going to give us free valet. They love me."

"Okay, but they're going to expect us to tip."

"Then tip, Fina. Don't be so stingy. The room is free with all my reward points, and I built this hotel; you can spare a few dollars for a tip."

"You need to stop saying you built this hotel, Mother. You literally only redesigned a wing of it."

She rolled her eyes. "This place was a total dump before I came in and fixed it. It was a roach motel basically, and now it's a five star hotel...because of me. So yes, Fina, I basically built this place and it would be nothing without me."

She always insisted on making me feel small.

"Just drive to the valet. Getting real tired of you."

The valet guys opened the door and my mother's face lit up. I watched her transform in front of the fresh-faced high school valet boys, like a butterfly breaking out of her cocoon.

183

The anger melted away and the setting sun cast a spotlight on her face. She smiled at them, and they smiled back.

"Sorry about the car, boys. Our Porsche is in the shop."

If by 'the shop' she meant repossessed, I thought.

I went to open the trunk, rolling my eyes as I heard the boys laughing. We hadn't even been out of the car for two minutes and she was already making them fall in love with her.

I struggled with the suitcase, my mom giving our purses to one of the boys to carry. They hung on to her every word. It was as if I didn't even exist.

"It's been so long since I've been here. God, I missed you guys."

The boys nodded, goofy smiles still plastered on their faces. "We missed you, too, ma'am," I heard one say. I was pretty sure they'd never even met her before.

"Call me Alice. Ma'am makes me sound old."

They laughed.

"Okay, well I'm going to go wait in the lobby, but my daughter is going to tip you real well!" She looked at me from the corner of her eye, a fake smile on her face as she walked inside. I wanted to get back in the car and run her over.

"That's me," I said, "the world's greatest fucking tipper." They didn't even hear me.

I went to reluctantly tip the boy holding my keys, but realized quickly that my mother had given our purses to the other boy who had followed her in.

I looked up at him, embarrassed. "Uh, hold on, sorry, my purse is inside."

He had lost the stars in his eyes and looked at me as though I was barely there.

"Yeah, okay. I'll just park the car real quick," he said.

"Okay, I'll be right back."

When I went inside, I noticed that the atmosphere had changed. The red-carpeted lobby was usually bustling with people going in and out, drinking, lounging. It was quiet now, a murmur of whispers and people huddled in corners. The group closest to me were wide-eyed, a mutual discomfort crossing their faces. I followed their gaze to see why they were whispering and saw that it was pointed directly at my mother. She stood at the front desk, looking visibly upset, the color drained from her face. Her foot tap, tap, tapped away. There was no one behind the front desk.

I heard a gasp, a small whisper of recognition, and someone from the group closest to me said, "Look! Her daughter is here, too."

Their faces turned to me, flashes of pity, anger, fear on their faces as I sunk into myself. As I tried to disappear.

I took a breath and walked past everyone, my eyes looking forward, my giant suitcase clunking slowly behind me.

"Mom," I whispered—god, it was so silent. "What's going on here?"

She bit her nails.

"I have no idea, Fina. This is so ridiculous. They said our reservation has been canceled."

"What do you mean canceled? I didn't cancel it…Did you?"

"Of course not! I walked in here and suddenly everyone was all up in a tizzy. I've been here dozens of times before! This is just BS. Canceling our reservation? You don't just do that. I built this place," she said, more to herself than anyone else, I thought.

"Okay, I'll try to talk to somebody, maybe the other desk. Hold on."

"Yeah," she said. "I'm going to go sit down. This is nuts. Tell them that."

I was searching for someone to talk to when a small, mousy woman came from the back with a nervous look on her face. She was only slightly taller than the top of the desk.

"Hi," I said. "Uh, what's going on? My mom said something about a canceled reservation?"

She looked up at me, recognizing the slant of my nose. The tousle of my hair. The shape of my eyes. I could tell she saw my mother in me.

"Uh, yeah, see, uh." She was sweating, her voice just as tiny as she was.

"I mean, I made the reservations, like, two months ago, and got the confirmation email."

I pulled it up on my phone and showed it to her.

"Yeah, the thing is, Frank, the owner, uh. He canceled it."

Body aches. Anxiety waves.

"He can't do that. He came to our house for dinner once! How can he do that?"

She flinched. I thought she might throw up.

"Well, ma'am, uh, you see it's kind of, it's bad publicity."

"Bad publicity? My mom and I have been coming here for years."

She took a big breath. "Yeah, um, exactly. Your mom has, well, we don't want to be associated with that, you know, thing."

"But she did so much work here. I mean, half of the right wing is entirely her design. She practically built this place! Your name is associated with that 'thing' either way!"

Heat on my face, clenched stomach.

"Well, technically, you're right. But having her stay, you know, uh, it doesn't help."

"Technically? No, this place was a dump before she…Are you? This is so—" I couldn't find any words. People were staring. "Okay, we'll just leave. Just have them, have them bring the car around."

I remembered when I heard that my mother was on the news. I had to find out about the broadcast from an old friend

rom high school. She called me when I was at work, telling
me to go online and check out the local news. My mother's
face was plastered all over the page.

The headline had made the front page of every newspaper
in town: "Well-Known Architect Leader of Ponzi Scheme."

I remember going to the bathroom at work and sinking to
the ground. I played the video over in my head a thousand
times. My mother covering her eyes as microphones pushed
in her face. My mother in handcuffs. My mother. I had never
cried so hard. I got so many calls that week, so many that I
just turned off my phone.

"I'm sorry for the inconvenience. I'm, uh, truly sorry."

The lady broke me out of my reverie. She was giving me
the look that I got every time I talked to someone who knew.
It was a look of wide-eyed sadness, a "bless her heart" sort of
embarrassment for me. In New York, I had managed to avoid
the stares. Here, I was surrounded by that same look. Over
and over again.

"Yeah," I said, laughing sarcastically. "I'm sure you really
are."

I walked over to where my mom was staring at the floor,
oblivious to all the people in the lobby whispering about her.

She looked up at me and smiled, that fake smile, lipstick
bright.

"Did you fix this mess?"

"No, Mom, we just. I'm sorry, but we have to go."

"What the hell do you mean we have to go?" Her voice
went from a whisper to a shout.

"Mom, shh, you're, you're being loud. Come on, they're
bringing the car around."

Her eyes got wild.

"They're not bringing the car around here. I am a paying
customer. They can't make us leave! I built this place! I built
it!" Tears filled her eyes. She was shaking.

People were gathering, staring as I tried to pull both he and my suitcase forward. I went numb, forgetting how to fee as my mother's voice got louder and louder, screaming abou the injustice of being treated so poorly.

"Mom, please. I know this is ridiculous, but we have to go You're making it worse. Please, Mom, come on!"

I was pulling at her, trying to get her out of there, but she was crying and yelling, pointing at the mousy lady behind the desk. I felt as if I had to protect her because she was my mother, because she was mine. I knew that it was okay to be upset at her for what she'd done, that was my right, but other people? That was something I couldn't take.

"And you! I know you, Cindy! I tipped you twenty-five dollars last time. Don't you remember?"

The woman, Cindy, stared at her, bewildered, and picked up the phone.

"Mom, they're going to call security. Please, Mom. Let's just leave."

I was pleading, my heart racing.

I saw two men in black suits coming from behind a door, walking toward us. My mother spotted them the moment I did.

"You're calling security on me? I can't believe this! I did nothing wrong!" She collapsed in my arms, sobbing, and I pulled her to the door. I was crying too, silent tears on my cheeks.

We walked outside, ignoring everyone around us.

The yellow Beetle sat in the roundabout, all alone, the valet boys nowhere to be found.

My suitcase wouldn't fit, so I took out the landlord's junk and left it on the curb. We got in the car and drove off, my mother sobbing as the sun disappeared behind the clouds.

***

The next morning, neither of us had gotten much sleep.

We stayed in a dingy motel where no one knew our names, or if they did, they didn't care. It was cheap and smelled like stale potato chips. The bed was hard, we found a dead roach and that was enough to keep us both awake, but we didn't talk about it. We weren't even pretending this time. We just didn't talk, and in the darkness, I felt my mother next to me, listening to her shallow breathing. I spent the night looking at the wall.

It was six a.m. when the alarm went off. My eyes felt as if I had just closed them. We got up slowly. Today was the day; we could feel it all over us.

My mother spent too long looking at herself in the mirror. I watched her hands clasp her pearls around her neck. She was staring at her reflection as if seeing it for the first time.

The Volkswagen Beetle stuck out like a sore thumb in the parking lot. Its faded yellow paint too colorful for the gray road and cloudy sky. I walked in front of my mom, got in the car, and put the key in the ignition.

She opened the passenger door and lowered her trembling body into the seat, placing her little black bag in her lap.

"Well, I guess this is it, huh?" she said.

"I guess so."

"Now you can finally be rid of me again. Ignore me for another seven."

She meant years. It was the first time she'd ever mentioned her sentence. It was the first time I'd even thought about it since I got here. Seven years. I repeated the number over in my head a few times.

"Mom. Please. Don't start this now."

"Well, you know, I called you so many times, Fina."

"I know."

"You know? You know and you didn't answer?"

I didn't know what to tell her. I didn't know why she was

189

bringing this up now, after all this time in the car, after last night. We were almost an exit away and she'd had so much time to talk to me before. Why now?

"I just—I couldn't."

"Why couldn't you? Do you know how lonely it's been without you?"

Her voice cracked and her eyes were welling with tears. I looked at the road and blinked back my own.

"Because of everything you've done, Mom. Everything you've ever done."

There was so much I needed to say to her but the words sat, hesitant, on the tip of my tongue, like a child afraid to jump off the diving board.

"Well, you hurt me. You hurt me so much, Fina."

Sadness turned to anger then. I felt as if she was blaming me for her sorrow and her pain, as if she was the only one in the world who felt those things.

"I may have hurt you, but you ruined me."

She gasped. I didn't know if I really meant it, but it felt good to say and that was enough.

***

Exit 64A, Kiesman Federal Prison, 1 Mile Ahead.
Neither of us spoke when we saw the sign.

I turned on the exit, the sound of the turn signal clicking far too loudly, and it seemed like neither of us were breathing. The road was long, foggy, nothing but a green, swampy marsh on either side. We were the only ones on the road, and I felt the weight of the two of us and the brevity of the silence that wrapped around us. We were both wiping away tear stains from our cheeks, my mother fiddling with her hair before she took off her pearls and put them in the backseat.

"I won't be able to keep these."

190

She wasn't talking to me, not really. She was just talking to talk—saying her own solemn goodbye to another part of herself that she'd be leaving behind.

"Do you—" My voice faltered. I cleared my throat. "Do you want me to keep them till you get out?"

"Do what you want, Fina."

Her voice seemed so small, distant, as if she had gone somewhere else, somewhere far away from here. I nodded and felt how quickly my heart was racing.

The prison entrance sat behind the fog at the end of the winding road. I had always thought there would be wire fences.

Instead there was just a sign, green grass, brown brick buildings, and a parking lot. There wasn't any wire anywhere. I looked over at my mom, the lipstick smeared a bit on her lips, at her hair up and her tired eyes.

"This is it," she said.

My mouth was dry. "This is it," I replied.

Neither of us moved. I expected her to say something, anything, but she just looked out onto the parking lot, a fresh set of tears brimming in her eyes.

"Mom? I—"

She cut me off. "I didn't want any of this, Fina. I didn't want any of this to happen to our lives."

"I know," I said.

"You know?"

We were looking at each other now.

"I know."

She nodded then, wiping the tears from her eyes, a small, somber smile playing at the corner of her mouth.

"You ready?" I asked

"I guess I have to be."

We exited the car and walked, side by side, toward the brown brick building on the hill.

DOGS OF THE CITY

SARAHANA SHRESTHA

DOGS OF THE CITY

Fixed outside tourist shops selling prayer wheels and mountain flights was a pack of boys in shirts shredding fast. Some days you saw them sprawled on the sidewalk, limbs tracing broken trajectories, eyes following specks of dust that might open to another universe. Other days you saw them trailing tourists for the day's income. Their feet sputtered, their arms arced, their tongues swam through languages: German, Hebrew, Spanish, Russian, French. Their faith—collapsing now, resurging then—rested on the first world's guilt for the third world's abandoned.

Bonding the days together was Dendrite: a cheap adhesive you throw into a plastic bag and inhale. This they did between everything else.

Leela was watching them from a café across the street, from the privileged position of a cappuccino on a terrace. A game of marbles seemed to be under way. She'd seen them for as long as she could remember—the median age constant, the boys ever-changing, as if on some mornings if you woke up a day too old, you left for a solitary swim like an aged whale readied for departure.

One boy sprang to his feet now and fired a string of obscenities at another, grabbing hardly anybody's attention under the traffic noise. He clutched the other's collar and shook him to the sway of fast-coming accusations. Something about stealing, something about his mother, something about being reborn as a dog. Others continued to flick at a marble, crack vulgar jokes, dance abruptly to a hit sing-along about falling in love.

The boy pushed the collar out of his grip and with it the accused, who landed a few feet away and found it efficient to stay there, body relaxed, eyes fixed on potential universe portals. The aggressor darted for a couple of tourists just out of a store. Tugging the man's backpack he yelled in a fit of high spirits, "Good afternoon, sir! Good afternoon, Madame!" They turned around in a haze of non-reactions, seeing that at most the boy was eleven, and at least, very poor.

"How much for a sweet song from me?" the boy asked in perfect English, mouth widened to a grin.

"What kind of a song?" the man asked curiously.

"You Italiano?" The boy slapped his palms together, dissecting the accent. Throwing his head back he leaped and yelled, "Del Pierrrrooo," flapping his arms, "Roberto Baggioooo." Then a scientist making a diagnosis, now a celebrator of the world's variety. "Si, si, Italiano," the couple was saying, but the boy was already running around them in circles, screaming, "Gooooaaaaal!"; screaming, "Viva Italie!"; screaming "Boungiornoooooo!"

Oh, mio Dio! They handed him a twenty.

"Grazie, Señor!" he said, still throwing his arms, "Grazie, Señora," now taking a bow. "Just enough to buy sugar for the cup of tea I'll be able to afford tomorrow. Ha! Ha!" His teeth still gleamed.

"Oh really?" said the man. "We've been drinking your milky tea for only ten bucks a cup."

"Maybe we should give you some recommendations," said the woman.

The boy had raised his arms mid-sentence, yelling over them, "Adios, mes amis! Boungiorno, mes cheries!" And, resorting to his native language, "May a big fat mosquito bite you on the ass. Ha! Ha! Ciao!"

Underneath a bridge that divided the city's temperament flowed a holy river thick with filth, decades-old. The modest squatter tents she'd seen on the riverbanks as a child had been replaced with concrete houses from which protruded dish antennae. Framing this view were large billboards advertising life insurance and cell phone plans.

At a street corner past the bridge, underneath the spotlight of a street lamp, two dogs hovered over a heap of trash, their lengthened breasts dangling low. The city in a snapshot, Leela thought, looking at them from behind and pulling out her camera phone. A step closer, and the dogs growled under tight teeth, turning their head just a degree in her direction, bellies still shielding the treasure.

"You know," she said, getting in her friend's car as it came around, "I used to want to go for a run when I lived here. I tried once, only to be chased by a pack of wild dogs."

"Wild?" said the friend. "You mean the opposite. The city belongs more to them than to us, don't you think? Their behavior is absolutely civilian, if you ask me. Think about it: their method of governance has outlived a monarchy, a democracy, and a civil war." They laughed.

There had been some talk of an organized effort to put away the stray dogs, who sometimes lunged even at walkers. A man was once seen outside the wall of his compound, lining it up with trash out of plastic bags.

"Good evening!" said a neighbor walking home. "What on earth are you up to?"

"Good evening, good evening," said the trash-liner, eager-explainer. "Our gatekeeper's gone to visit his wife in the village, you see. I'm lining the wall here with trash so the dogs come and guard us for the night, eh?"

Somewhere in the city was a close observer who'd seen the number of street dogs already decline. One day the city will look, he thought, and find the streets without canines; they'll be missed not for a second.

Elsewhere in the city was a girl of about eight who'd lifted a stray pup onto her lap, as had done many others before.

On her way home from dinner one night, Leela was approaching the same tourist shops, their shutters being pulled. The sidewalk was marked with puffs of steam rising from carts selling dumplings. She stopped to film a vendor who was breastfeeding an infant, their portrait heaving in and out of the hot mist.

She pushed toward a coffee shop and saw the boys, still camped across the street. The way their eyes lacked direction, the way their limbs floated at the speed of a cloud, they might as well have been zombies.

Halfway up the stairs to the café, she turned around. On the sidewalk she pointed the camera at the pack. She was bringing the viewfinder into focus when she heard a thud in her stomach, sensed a pair of vampire fangs snap from a boy's mouth. He was already a few feet from her, lunging, slithering between cars. In a tick of panic she searched his face for the names of Italian soccer players; for the joke about saving up to buy a cup of tea for which he already had the sugar. But all she saw were fangs and claws; vampire and zombie.

He pounced on the camera and left a bloody hairline on her arm.

"Must pay to film!" he yelled, trying to loosen her grip. "Homeless boys sniffing glue, oh what a hit at your movie festivals! Must pay, sister!"

A few others were staggering across the street. Twisting and panting, she said: "What the hell do you know about movie festivals anyway?"

He let go and stood there growling with furious eyes, tilting his head up to look at hers.

"Seriously," she said, "what do you know about movie festivals?"

"You think you're the first one?" he said. "We have a fee! And you must pay it! Or else we take the camera!"

By now it was eight arms pulling and pinching at hers.

"Stop, stop, I'll give you the money!" she screeched.

"Don't give them any money, sister!" a young man said, coming out of a restaurant behind her. "Have you seen their eyes? Red like tomatoes! Useless thieves! Scoot, you little roaches! They're welcome at the kids' shelter, sister. Free food, clean clothing, warm bed. Why don't you fatten yourselves up, learn a letter or two, and get a job, eh?"

"Oy, you hero," said the boy to the man, raising a plank of a palm with bony fingers, looking like a miniature thirty-year-old. "A little free food doesn't close the book on life's accounts, okay? A pillow in a tight room of roaches is no fairy tale, my friend. No need to tell me about the free meals, I'm there at ten every—"

"Life's accounts?" the man was spitting. "Life's accounts?"

Leela was wrestling with her moral bearings.

"A free meal doesn't kill an appetite," the boy was saying, "it feeds the appetite. Makes it stronger! Ha! Ha! I'm not an idiot. Don't pretend like you live differently. Whatever you can get, get more of it. That's the goal of life, mister!"

A small crowd had stalled around them, amused, unalert.

"They'll drop dead any day," the man was saying. "Look at their eyes. Red like tomatoes."

As had been tradition in her last few visits, the final night would be spent at a temple square, staying up to watch the sunrise. Her friends had brought some beer, which they were now offering to the two policemen huddled around a fire.

"Oh no, sir, we can't," they said, declining.

The group was seated on the temple's steps, looking out to a dark field of what would've been red bricks, brown roofs, and blue hills. The conversation, often culling biographic details from the policemen—which village they'd come from, how old they were—was punctuated by dog howls from all directions.

"I think one pack is getting closer," Leela said, listening closely.

"They're definitely having a real dialogue," a friend replied, cupping an ear.

Sometimes it sounded as if the dogs ran in unison, came to a halt, transmitted their location in a chorus of howls, and received an answer in an echo more distant.

Leela gasped as a pack entered from an alley to the right. They ran past in a pitter-patter of paws, paying no mind to the humans.

"The city belongs to the dogs," one of the policemen said, spreading his palms against the fire. "They behave like they run it."

"I'm surprised the glue-sniffing boys haven't joined forces with them," Leela said. "They should pair up like those Nigerian handlers with their chained hyenas." She recalled the photographs she'd seen: men keeping tradition, the hyenas their partners in street entertainment.

"Homeless boys with dancing stray dogs," a friend suggested.

"They'd probably get the dogs sniffing glue, too," someone else said.

Maybe they had some kind of an agreement between them: one side of the bridge each.

It was against the spirit of the whole thing to consult a watch for time. In the dark you'd hear the first movements of rising farmers: water running in public baths, metal containers clinking, phlegm gathering in distant throats, half-asleep greetings in the local dialect.

This was how you knew the sky was readying itself for a rising sun.

Someone mentioned the squatters on the riverbank were

going to be evicted soon.

"Is that true?" they asked the policemen.

"One day they'll have to be. It's not legal, after all," was the reply. But the group had gotten quieter as the night receded, a diminished conversation magnifying the stereoscopic soundtrack of the neighborhood's awakening. Slithering light was beginning to outline faraway shapes. They hadn't heard the dogs in a while.

"I guess they sleep after all."

Leela set her camera on a tripod and watched the silhouette of a farmer's bullock cart. It was trudging toward the horizon on the shoulders of two buffalos, slowly gathering details against a goldening sky. Soon the tea shops would open, blackened kettles puffing atop blackened stoves.

Dear Craig

Daniela Bizzell

SCAN HERE!

DEAR CRAIG

You never fuck a woman more than twice. You fuck her more than two times and you're stuck. You'll smell her everywhere. Lavender and baby powder and raspberry lip balm. That shit will stick to your nose and haunt you while you sleep. It'll make you breathe out your mouth.

***

Meet her on the corner of S State Street and E 44th, near the drug store where Loose and Rex try to steal Colt 45's and barbeque pork rinds. Stay outside; Sheena still works there, and those plastic red nails are sure to scratch you up all over if she sees your face again. Suck on a cigarette as she walks by, smooth. Lean back as you stare at her ass—like a peach, ticking left and right as if it's on some sort of spring.

"Mama, where you headed so quick, you ain't givin' me and that body time to get acquainted."

Wait for her to turn around. Wait for a smile. Wait for a slap. Wait for anything. If she does nothing, say something else.

"You think that'll get you pussy? Screaming at girls until they climb on ya dick?"

Laugh at her because you think she's funny. Laugh at her because in twenty-three years of trying to get a phone number on a shitty Chicago sidewalk, you've never heard someone respond to you like that. Laugh at her because she's strong and it makes you feel weak.

"I'm not trying to do nothing, baby, just saying hello." Try not to stare for too long, but make sure she knows you're looking. Wait a little bit when you get past her tits; she's got a caramel-colored stomach, a little heart tattoo on her hipbone. "That heart for anyone special?"

"Your mother must not have taught you shit if you think that's how you say hello to a lady."

Don't let her see you wince. Don't think about your mom. Don't get angry. You're not trying to scare her away this quick.

"Nah, she must not have." Chase after her a little when she starts to walk away, but stay back. "You never told me who that heart was for." Whisper into her ear, and give her chills through this July heat.

"It's not for anyone but me."

"So, that means someone else can snag it?" Lay back a little when she doesn't smile. Most of these girls smile when you say something cute.

Keep walking a little when Loose and Rex come sprinting out of the store. Ignore them while she's still around. Ask her for a phone number. Tell her that you like a challenge. When she says no, tell her you hang around here on Saturday nights, sometimes you hit up Chauncey's down on E 41st, if she ever needs to find you. When she doesn't say anything, ask for her name. Step in front of her while she's still walking so she has to look at you. Stick your hand out as if you're in church and say, "Craig." When she smiles, just a small smile, and shakes your hand back, repeat her name in your head over and over, "Andrea," but her friends call her, "Drea."

After that, leave. Meet your boys over at the park and barely say goodbye. Leave her wanting a little more, leave her with that handshake.

***

You'll see her a few other times before you're back at her place, feeling her pink sheets on your skin, smelling that lavender, trying not to cum too quick because she's the flyest girl you've ever been with. And you'll be here again, won't you? Right up against her smooth, warm skin for the next few years, and that smell will stick to your clothes, you hair, your mouth. She'll be following you around whether you like it or not.

***

Buy her dollar Hennessy at Chauncey's and watch her face turn a little pink, wait for that hardness she loves showing off to melt away. Don't talk too much; she doesn't need to know you. But listen. Listen to what she says when she's a little too drunk, wobbling to the bathroom in shiny black high heels and skin tight jeans that go up to her belly button. They love when you listen. Do a small bump when she's in there. You know you'll be up for a while.

Remember that she lives with her mom and works at a little beauty shop in the city, selling makeup to teenagers with more money than they know what to do with. Remember that her dad left back when she was five or six; another woman, a crack addict, lost his job. It's one of the above and either way he's not around, which is a good thing. Dads never like you. Just keep listening, let her let you in, let her keep sipping on her drink even though it's just melted ice cubes, let her put her hand on your thigh. You want to be cute, keep things light, so don't remind her that it took you three tries to get her to come out.

Watch her as she climbs to the third floor of her building, stumbling every now and then, that ass still ticking like some sort of clock. Everything's dark, but you can tell her place looks clean, as if a family lives in it; it smells as though someone's been cooking—sweet onions, fresh bread—it makes you think about the last time you ate.

Keep your shirt on when you're on top of her, feeling her sheets on your bare legs. She's the kind of girl that'll push you right off if she sees track marks even if you've only tried shit a few times; when she tries to pull it off, stop her. Tell her she should be the one taking off her clothes. That'll make her feel good about herself.

It's three a.m. when you finish, both of you breathing hard and fast. She's trying to hold your hand, but you tell her you've got things to do. Put on your pants before she can say anything. Expect her to start fighting it, calling you a jackass, just another hoodrat trying to get his dick wet. But she doesn't. She turns her naked back to you and tells you to lock the door on your way out. You never fuck her twice, even if you want to smell that lavender on your skin one more time.

Leave. Leave because it's easy. Leave because you haven't gotten high in seven hours. Leave because she doesn't stop you. Lock the door on your way out.

Your mom is passed out on the sofa when you get home. Half a cigarette floating in a plastic cup, a couple sips of gin left in it. You walk into your bedroom to find Eddie in your bed, no sheets, no pillow, a charred up spoon on the table next to it. You want to shake him, ask where your shit is, how much he took; even if he is a dope-fiend he'll take anything that'll get him high. But you don't want to touch his greasy wife beater, his sweat-covered skin. Instead, you check his pockets, finding a half-packed Ziploc and a couple of bucks he'll forget he ever had.

Sit on the old recliner in the living room after you take the cup out of your Mom's hand. Scream at her in the morning about her scummy-ass boyfriend sleeping in your bed, but don't do it tonight, you don't have enough energy. Peel your shirt off and sit for a second. The heat in this place makes you feel as if you're in hell, plus it makes the trash piles in the kitchen stink up the whole apartment. All you need now are some flames and you're living it.

Grab the pipe from the table and sit back. Half pack it, just enough to get you buzzed, not enough to keep you up all night.

When you get everything ready, you feel smart, like a scientist, you don't think of anything else. Once it's done, you feel happy; your skin feels kind of cool. Pop in the new Run DMC tape into your Walkman, the one that just came out. Keep it low, but loud enough. Tap, tap, tap along to every beat. You want to know every word on the album before the week is up.

After an hour, let your eyes close. Fall asleep dreaming about Drea. Think you can still taste raspberry on your mouth.

***

You swore you wouldn't do it again. She feels worse than the drugs you use, so good and so bad, a pulse in your head that keeps you from falling asleep at night. It only took one more time for you to get hooked, one more feel of those cool sheets against her hot skin, got one more taste, drank too much Henney, let her know who you were, just for a minute. You can't get the smell of her shampoo out of your head, even if you go weeks without seeing her. Try not to, but get stuck.

***

Get a construction job in the city because Drea's eight months pregnant and you're still spending money on half-grams of cut blow and late nights. Empty your pockets Thursday night, show her your arms because she doesn't trust you anymore, not since she found out about your bad habits after she got pregnant. Let her scream about HIV, the police, and how she doesn't want any child of hers growing up with a crackhead father. Go to Chauncey's and do a bump in the bathroom that Rubin, the bartender, hooks you up with. Take advantage of Thursday's happy hour.

While you're outside sucking on a cigarette, pretend you never met her. Pretend you're still doing you, drinking forties in the park with Loose and Rex, smoking blunts and macking on girls that just got out of high school. Think about your hell and how it almost feels good to look back at it, to watch Eddie punch a hole in the wall right next to that shitty twenty-inch TV, to see your mom collect beer cans so she can make a quick buck. Seeing the same thing over and over again feels right. There isn't any change in hell and the same-old shit feels good. Walk back to her place; you have to stay there now because it's getting time and there's no way she's doing this by herself.

She's asleep on the couch, only wearing a sports bra and boxer shorts, hands resting on her belly. It still has the same caramel color and you can see the heart, another one sitting right next to it, for you. Pick her up. Her belly's big, but she's still small, plus that bump makes you feel like Superman. Put her in bed and go into the living room, listen to your Walkman, wait for that come down you know is on its way. Keep things quiet because her mom's asleep in one room and she's asleep in the other; they're light sleepers and you know you won't get away with anything anymore. Breathe so light that you can't even tell if you're alive or not. Don't bother taking your boots off; you have to wake up in four hours anyway.

***

After Sean is born, take Loose up on his offer to go into business. Convince yourself that with a baby, you need a lot more money than you have and Drea shouldn't have to work so much and money is important. Look at Sean one morning and get kind of teary-eyed because he's always smiling and you didn't know babies could smile this much or this early in the morning. Play your tapes in the living room when he's falling asleep in your arms that night. Touch his curly brown hair and feel as if you love Drea more because he exists. Cut down on the blow because they're making your nose bleed and you don't want her to worry. Hide your pipe in a rolled up pair of socks you only wear when Drea wants you to get dressed up—the black cotton Calvin Klein socks that she found at Macy's half-off. Convince yourself that as long as you can pay the heat bill, the electricity, diapers, and a night out every now and then, she doesn't need to know what you do when you're not around.

Get familiar. Don't be stupid. Tell yourself that you're a professional now. Learn. Teach yourself.

Make about eighty bucks a gram selling pure cocaine. In the city, sell mainly eight balls and make about two hundred. Head down to the projects to sell crack rocks. Ten a bag. But the crackheads come back like crackheads and you sell three hundred bags a night. Don't feel guilty. You're making money to survive. Drea asks where it all comes from. Tell her Bruce is giving you a raise at this new site. Tell her you won a lotto card. Tell her you've been saving up. Know she doesn't believe you. Stop caring. She has.

***

Give yourself a bump in the morning. No more, no less. Start with a buzz to get through the day. Make enough to afford a place outside of the complex. Make enough to get your-

211

self a car that not only runs but looks good when you're driving it, a black Mazda, cheap and fun. Make enough so Drea only works at the boutique four days out of the week. When she's at work, take four-year-old Sean with you to run errands after you pick him up from school.

Know that he's fine eating McDonald's in the back seat, playing with a plastic Kermit the Frog that came in the bright, red box; watch him stick it in the front pocket of his polo shirt that Drea always puts him in. Play your music for him. Teach him something. Public Enemy, Whodini; watch him bob his head in his car seat, sipping on a juice box.

"Hey, little man, you like what you're hearing?"

Watch him move his head up and down, a mouth full of French fries.

Bring him to Chauncey's in the middle of the day; his school goes until three. Everyone loves little Seany, and you let him put dimes in the jukebox while you sip something strong and talk to Loose about profits. Watch him while people step up to you, looking for a quick fix. Tell them that your son is here and this shit can't happen right now, there's a time and a place. Then tell Loose to watch Sean and sell a quick bag in the bathroom. Check your pager. Remember that Drea makes you answer her pages now. She made you get that pager in the first place after the first time you took Sean out and didn't come home until one in the morning. Call her from the pay phone in the bar and tell her you'll be home in an hour. You have to run an errand. She screams to bring Sean home before you run any more fucking errands. Tell her it's not like that, you just have to change the oil in the car. She stops asking questions, but tells you she's counting that hour down to the minute. Tell her that she's acting crazy. Tell her that you love her. Tell her you won't be late.

When you get home, play with Sean on the carpet in the living room while Drea looks at the both of you. Don't say

212

anything when she says that she should leave your ass because she's sick of having a heart attack every time she comes
home and the baby isn't there. Nod your head and go out for
a cigarette.

Pretend again. Pretend your life is different. Pretend all
of your money didn't go to trips to the dentist and clothes
that the baby grows out of every two months. Pretend that
you could do whatever you wanted in your own home without anyone telling you different. Pretend you never met her.
Your heart hurts for a lot of different reasons. The baby makes
you want to live better, you love calling yourself Daddy, acting like the responsible one in the group of clowns you call
friends. You have an authority that they don't have. That they
don't want. Drea makes you love, a painful love that makes
you hate yourself but makes you feel like dying every time
you think about being away from her.

Lay in bed next to her a few hours later. She's half-asleep,
but you're antsy and your legs won't stop moving. Press yourself up against her. Make her want you like she used to. Kiss
her neck and smell the lavender that made you keep coming
back. Your leg can't stop twitching. Finally, she turns around.
Remember she helps you stop thinking, makes things a little
easier in those few seconds. Fall asleep with her head on your
chest.

***

Switch up the business on Sean's fifth birthday. Dope is
becoming a nineties drug, cheaper and easier to get to, and
Loose offers you a new position. Spend the day in the projects
seeing how well you can push this new shit. Call after girls
that look barely eighteen and offer some free product. They
get hooked faster when they're younger. Notice the girl with
the tattoo on her chest. A rose with the name Damian wrapped

213

around the stem.

"Baby, looks like this Damian kid might be someone to worry about."

"He ain't shit, just some punk."

Look at her for a second; just long enough to make her arms cross and her lips twitch.

Watch her get nervous and break eye contact. You know she's weak; you could get away with anything.

"You got a car, baby?"

"I got a job to do; I can't fuck with you right now." Say you have all sorts of important shit to do, but know that she's starting to make your skin crawl. Remember the first time you met Drea. Remember her tattoo. Pick Sean up from daycare at three.

Take Sean to a little playground near the old complex where you grew up, where your mom used to take you. Feel for those days when she pushed you on a squeaky swing and called you, "Eggo." Give him a toy Firebird you got at Toys R Us while you're there because you want him to have all sorts of presents today. Watch him play with it, make car sounds with his mouth, and drive it down the slide. Stay until it's dark and you can't see the ground underneath you. Race Sean to the car, but fall back because you're breathing gets heavy and your bones feel weak. You need something and you're starting to forget what that something is.

Cut into the Save-A-Lot chocolate cake Drea bought that afternoon. Give Sean his first Walkman and tell him he can borrow your albums anytime he wants. Watch him hold it in his hand and smile because he doesn't really know what he's holding. Ignore Drea's dirty look, it's okay that a five-year-old has one. He'll grow into it. The apartment is full of albums now and one day he can have them. When everything is settled, tell Sean that Dad has to go to work, tell Drea you have to get out of the house, that business is calling and you have to pay the bills. Read her face, know what she's feeling. Fight with her because you feel like shit and she's the only one that'll take it. Tell her you've got more important things to do, but glance over at Sean who has his headphones on, playing nothing in his ears, while he runs the Firebird over the shag carpet.

Get angry because Drea knew what she was getting into when she started things up with you. Get angry because you're always doing shit for this family and being such a good dad for Sean and maybe for once you don't want a fight, you just want to go and make money because the dentist already looked at Sean's teeth coming in and said he'll probably need braces. Let the conversation get loud and out of hand. You don't know why everything seems so bad right now but you feel as if you're drowning in this house.

Go into the sock drawer and pull out the pipe because you know she won't pull it out of your hands. Walk into the kitchen and watch her eyes get big. Feed off it. Let it make you angry. Whisper when she yells. Tell her to stop acting like some sort of child and that she'll make Sean upset. But it's too late. Sean's in the kitchen, clutching on to his Walkman, his headphones around his five-year-old neck. Watch Drea's head turn so Sean can't see her cry. Feel Sean tug at your jeans and ask if he can have more cake because he hasn't brushed his teeth yet and it's still his birthday. He's still smiling and you wish you could be more like him. Wish you could have taken a picture every time he smiled.

Cut him a slice and send him back to the living room. Don't say anything when Drea tells you if you leave, she doesn't want you to come back. Look for an old hoodie to wear while she tells you that she's fed up with this no-good lifestyle. Punch a hole in the drywall right next to the refrigerator when she says you'll end up dead just like your mother. Watch her eyes get big again, eyes so big it's as if she's been blind this entire time and you just gave her sight.

Remind yourself over and over that you aren't a monster. Walk over and kiss Sean on the forehead and pretend you don't see Drea crying in the background. Put your hoodie on and tell Sean to be good for Mommy and don't stay up too late. Let him look up at you and smile, then yell to his mom that he wants to watch just a little bit of TV before bed. Pass her by in the kitchen, your arm grazing hers.

Keep walking. Leave because it's easy. Leave because you haven't gotten high in seven hours. Leave because she doesn't stop you. Lock the door on your way out.

SELECTED POETRY

AUDREY ZEE WHITESIDES

SCAN HERE!

DEMONS FASCINATED
TOO SOON

After Akilah Oliver

Waiting on the bus
waiting on the bus
am I dressed for possession
meaning ownership
(come back to ghosts later)
with a bifurcated voice
parallel down middle
a big bowling split
in right-mindedness
a religion of inquiry
a family waiting
on the busted speaker
the busted speaker gets right
right back
off her back with
taxes & arise-shine wanderlust
while the road
(the burns the road)
the company paid
v. the company due
and if you need anything
call me back right
if you need
beyond the hot-house
(a singer attraction:
intensity of the hungry)

rut business &
the archive wasn't quick enough
we dressed frenzied
our friends were unbeknownst
to us friends
& public.

NEEDED IDIOTICS

For Mia Brune

Glory gives me constancy
toward Earth.
Complete friends &
collaborationists
late religious
bubbles of conversation.
We needed to raise
wilful spaces to think
just one desire through
its martial pratfalls,
marital readership
such a beautiful event
pound some dock girlfriend
with me, ok.

Comparative deities don't even have
to be animalistic for you
I stopped speaking for my glory
when I was no teen, my bro
dispossessed my contacts.
Out of lights, date anyone
No teen meant swanly
The woman stretching arms
asked & got a basement

before which rites ballooned
Requirements give glory
seen woman
Mine dearness museum
breakneck English through the curve
Cut kids for latches,
tutor reaction back into our glory.

EMERGENCY AM I

The revolutions of emergency dancers
you see tonight
will perhaps remind you of yr body
but who's to say they wouldn't
or will this reminder lead
to productive fear?
I care,
trauma attention through price-checker.

Popping out time
wants you madly, babe,
pop me in the alley before you go
I want you to make me
make you breakfast on knees
who else would I go to
now time cannot be
managed humanely
extralegal subject
seem less violent than other

---

distant state prod state
state state dry state
pull member turn member
state member speech member
end hairs intimate hairs
penalty hairs intimate hairs

force become harrow become
work become sadden become
I egged my distance
at you, it worked.

USA GIRLS #666

Someone has given my mother
a "mobile phone" and she is
eating all the planet's dirt.
Would you put her in a room?
Would my mother be put
in room
enough for barter economy
when she knows
"Russians"
are a dead half of a marriage,
forget their politics.

Experimental credit card knife-like
for her,
its less ambiguous
cocktail chestpiece.
This one's the "punk song"
I will tell you
what God
has had you divined in ashes
elbow to cunt
to put in a sharp mom
constant satellite of tapes.
It will be hard for us to communicate
if you've never rhymed "city" and "shitty"
or sang along to a song that does.

Hospital Part

Finally, I felt out of print
sad monster waiver and you
like everyone
destroy some women you never meet,
but which gamble thank you will get you
a private recovery bed
yr hand has been lost
I felt worthwhile of piracy,
so now we both work for lesbians.

Next step my bank account a Tumblr seance,
that is, never getting better
pain for senators,
pain-comics for DIY,
crawled a bitch for DIY,
to no-difference-but blues,
or a mix,
or like finally cutting
is on my provider,
this poem written early morning
of Dyke March 2013
may I come back to this poem,
crowdbased never,
beddy-baby later,
that's an attractive life plan.

FIN.

SPONSORS

TSS
THE SHORT STORY

he *Short Story* was established in 2015 and has developed
to an influential platform, championing short stories, flash
ction, and micro-fiction. Our aim is to publish the best
ontemporary short stories and flash fiction in the English
nguage, and provide news and views on short fiction.

COMPETITIONS & AWARDS:

e host a *short story competition* every quarter with prize money of £650
encourage writers and their use of the short story form. We also have a
onthly *flash fiction competition* with a £50 prize.

eanwhile, our *TSS Young Writers Awards* – one to be given each month
2016 – provide the opportunity for emerging writers to gain commission,
ublishing credit, and publicity. Please do pass the word on.

FEATURES:

Our fantastic contributors, who range from published authors to emerging
riters, engage with the short form on both creative and academic levels. We
ublish a variety of features including:

Interviews
Essays on Short Fiction
Reviews
Editing tips & Critiques

ollow us:
ww.theshortstory.co.uk | Twitter @ShortStory2000 | shortstory2000.
umblr | Pinterest @theshortstory | instagram @theshortstory.co.uk